EXPLAINING THE ATOM

"There is no possibility of telling whether the issue of scientists' work will prove them to be fiends, or dreamers, or angels."

—LORD RAYLEIGH

EXPLAINING

THE ATOM

BY SELIG HECHT

WITH REVISIONS AND
ADDITIONAL MATERIAL

BY EUGENE RABINOWITCH

NEW YORK · THE VIKING PRESS

Originally published in 1947
Revised edition published in 1954
New edition, with further revisions and additional material,
published in 1964 in a
Viking Compass Edition
Issued by The Viking Press, Inc.
625 Madison Avenue, New York, N.Y. 10022

Third Printing September 1970

Published simultaneously in Canada by
The Macmillan Company of Canada Limited

SBN 670-30217-1 (hardbound)
SBN 670-00167-8 (paperbound)

Library of Congress catalog card number: 64-25531
Printed in U.S.A. by The Colonial Press Inc.

For Celia

For Celia

CONTENTS

LIST OF ILLUSTRATIONS

FOREWORD TO THE REVISED EDITION

Selig Hecht, professor of biophysics at Columbia University, died in 1947 at the early age of fifty-five. He was not only a great scholar in his field (biophysics; more particularly, the physics of vision), but a man of rare compassion for the sufferings of his fellow men and deep concern for the fate of mankind. When it was suggested to me that I bring up to date his book *Explaining the Atom,* I accepted this task as a duty and a pleasure—a duty to the memory of a man whose spontaneous sympathy, friendship, and assistance were so generously given to me when I first came to America and felt lost in the human sea of New York; and a pleasure in being associated with what I believe is a classic of popular scientific writing, so simple and yet so precise, exciting as a thriller, and yet uncompromising in its integrity and conviction.

Dr. Hecht wrote this short book in 1946 out of a deep apprehension for the future. In common with many scientists, he felt that the release of atomic energy had ushered in not only a new era of science and technology, but also, and above all, an era that would bring an unprecedented test of the wisdom of nations and their leaders. Can mankind, faced with the destructive capacities of atomic weapons, break with the age-old tradition of international rivalries and enmities, and put an end to naked power conflicts between states? This was the challenge. As a true scientist, Hecht believed that the basis of all wisdom is knowledge, and that only if people are brought to understand what the atom is, and why the release of its energy calls for a fresh beginning in human affairs, can they begin to solve the problems with which the atomic age confronts them. Not that this knowledge alone is sufficient to insure peace and security among nations; but it is a prerequisite without which no rational search for salvation is possible. In this belief, "atomic scientists" launched in 1945 and 1946 their campaign to make America and the world aware of the implications of atomic energy; and it was in this belief that Selig Hecht, not an "atomic scientist" himself, brought to the campaign his unique gift for clear, simple, and convincing exposition of science.

The fight begun in 1945 between scientific enlightenment, which calls for an end to all wars as the only way to survive in the atomic age, and the stubborn heritage of international anarchy, reinforced in our time by the rule of a fanatic totalitarianism over a large part of the globe, has not gone well since. Selig Hecht, who had suffered, as from a personal grief and injury, from the aggressive cruelty and fanaticism let loose upon Europe by the totalitarian madness of Germany, and the vast holocaust of the Second World War in which this madness inexorably ended, has not lived to follow, in renewed anguish, the breakdown of the attempts to establish international control of atomic energy, and the headlong rush of the world into the atomic arms race. He was spared seeing the advent of the still more horrifying thermonuclear weapons. Other scientists who are witnessing this drift of civilized mankind toward self-destruction have no right to become fatalistic and indifferent, and to abandon the efforts to which Hecht had so ardently and effectively devoted himself. They must not cease to believe in the power of rational knowledge and objective truth, and its ultimate victory over the irrational forces of stubborn tradition and reckless fanaticism. May the new edition of *Explaining the Atom* do its share, as the first two did, in spreading more widely the knowledge of the atom, and with it the understanding of the ways, aims, and possibilities of science. May it help more people to comprehend how we have come to fathom the nature and structure of the atom; and how by this understanding, mankind has been given the power to use the immense energies so long locked in the atomic nucleus, for whatever purpose it may see fit—destroying itself in atomic war, or building a more prosperous and secure world.

EUGENE RABINOWITCH

Urbana, Illinois
June 28, 1954

PREFACE TO THE FIRST EDITION

This is a book for the complete layman. It follows the steps
that were taken historically in going from the earliest
questions about the nature of common substances to the
large-scale liberation of atomic energy. The number of these
steps is small, and the ideas involved are simple. They can
be described in all their essentials without assuming any
knowledge of physics, chemistry, and mathematics. I have
done this before in five lectures at the New School for Social
Research in New York to an audience most of whom had had
no training in any science. The steps are explicitly stated in
the Table of Contents and form a skeleton summary of the
story.

The reader is urged to go through the book in a few
sessions. He is advised to read easily and steadily, and not to
struggle with any part that seems unclear; most likely it will
become clear later. The point is to read ahead and to get
the full sweep of the narrative. If after a first rapid reading
one has any impulse toward rereading, the temptation should
not be resisted. The reward of a second reading is dispro-
portionately large in pleasure and profit.

I did not work on any project connected with the atomic
bomb; my war work dealt with light and vision. My knowledge of atomic physics comes from public sources. All the

scientific information secured before 1940 is available in books and professional articles. Between 1940 and 1945 papers on atomic physics were not published. Since then there has been the official Report on Atomic Energy by H. D. Smyth; and now there has begun again a slow trickle of professional papers. What I understand, thousands of professional people know. I hold no secrets.

This book could easily have been ten times its size, with all the details, diagrams, and equations to make it scholarly and complete, and all without recourse to secret information. It is a thin book so that it will easily convey to the layman the intellectual drama of the developments in physics during the last fifty years. This needs no apparatus of scholarship.

My purpose is to supply a background against which people can think and act intelligently on the problems of atomic energy. So long as one supposes that this business is mysterious and secret, one cannot have a just evaluation of our possession and security. Only by understanding the basis and development of atomic energy can one judge the legislation and foreign policy that concern it. I hope that this book will help to make intelligent voters.

SELIG HECHT

Golden Farm, Bridgewater, Connecticut
September 10, 1946

EXPLAINING THE ATOM

PROLOGUE

Before dawn on July 16, 1945, a group of scientists and military men met in a deserted region of New Mexico to make a scientific experiment. The men arranged themselves so that some were 25 miles from a central tower and some about 10 miles. The persons nearest the tower were in a timber-and-earth observation shelter 7 miles away.

At a given moment someone closed a switch that started a series of events controlled by machinery installed for this purpose. The end of this series was that at a prearranged moment there occurred a tremendous flash of light, followed immediately by a strong surge of heat, and some seconds later by a loud rumbling noise. One observer, who lay flat on the ground 10 miles from the explosion, with his head down and only his neck exposed, said that it felt as if a hot iron had been held next to his skin. The first atomic bomb had been exploded.

A few weeks later the next atomic bomb was exploded over Hiroshima, and a while later a third, over Nagasaki. Since then Americans have exploded hundreds of experimental bombs in the air, underground, and underwater, on Bikini Atoll and Eniwetok Island in the Pacific, and on the

3

Yucca Flats Proving Grounds in Nevada. Many atomic explosions in Soviet Russia have been picked up by monitors abroad. Great Britain exploded her first bomb in 1952 on an island off the west coast of Australia, and France followed suit with test explosions in the Sahara desert. We have all become familiar with the appearance of an above-ground atomic explosion: the mushroom-shaped cloud rising perhaps 40,000 feet into the air, the shattered and burned-out houses, and the weirdly distorted steel structures extending for miles from the spot straight under the explosion center ("ground zero"). Almost equally familiar is the awe-inspiring sight of the mile-wide column of water rising into the air from an underwater atomic explosion and breaking into deadly radioactive spray.

In Hiroshima 50,000 people were killed immediately, and of those who survived a like number died soon after. Years later, some were still dying. There is no way of knowing how long the effects of this bomb will last. Although the average health of survivors of the Hiroshima and Nagasaki explosions is now normal, and their offspring show no alarming deviations from normality, it is by no means certain that subtle genetic changes will not become apparent in future generations; and this genetic danger to the race would become much greater if a much larger proportion of a nation were to be exposed to nonlethal doses of radiation, as is likely to happen in a future war.

Since those fateful weeks in 1945 the world has had no rest from the atomic bomb, as its international and domestic implications have become clearer to an astonished but unprepared public. The multitude of articles, pamphlets, and discussions has dissipated the more absurd ideas about atomic energy and exposed the real problems and some of their possible solutions. But many ridiculous ideas remain, particularly those concerning the origin, the nature, and the secrets of atomic energy.

In some experience with atomic-energy legislation, I have talked with enough public men to know that almost none of them understands even the elementary principles underlying the release of atomic energy. The same is true for most well-educated laymen. And yet all of us must make decisions about this weapon, which "is potentially destructive beyond the wildest nightmare of the imagination." These decisions cannot be made in ignorance; the public must be informed.

Consider the matter of secrets, of which there is still too much talk. As this book shows, there is no unique or single secret about atomic energy or even about atomic bombs. However, among the many bills passed by Congress, in 1946, one provided the death penalty for giving away *the* secret of the atomic bomb. Such behavior assumes that the release of atomic energy happened suddenly without any previous history. Indeed, many people still believe this, and the newspaper stories have helped to encourage such belief. There lingers among us the idea that an inventor, a scientist, a professor, is a long-haired gentleman, a little wild in the head, who has crazy ideas which occasionally work out. The atomic bomb presumably was one of those that worked.

As a matter of fact the scientists of the Manhattan District were generally known as the longhairs. One of my friends who was a consultant for the atomic bomb project began to make regular visits to the barber and to take them very seriously. He explained that as a professor his hair made little difference to him or to his colleagues as long as it looked decent, but when he had to deal with the Army men, he insisted that at least the physical excuse for being called a longhair be absent.

The popular story has it that one of these longhairs, seconded by no less a longhair than Albert Einstein, managed to tell President Roosevelt about his idea for an atomic bomb. He estimated the cost at about two billion dollars, and the President, being a sporting man with excellent judgment, took this gigantic gamble, and appointed a general to direct the production of the bomb. The general then hired scientists and engineers, and built laboratories and factories; and sure enough, he constructed a bomb, to the discomfiture of the Japanese and the greater glory of American industry.

This whole conception—the secret of the longhair, the President's gamble, and the position of the general—is wrong. It is wrong for several reasons. The notion of atomic energy is nothing new; it has been investigated and discussed by thousands of people for years. Even the actual words have long been in use. For about fifty years scientists have been working in this area, and innumerable papers have been published about it. As we shall see, the subject has had an orderly history and development, which a host of people all over the world knew and understood. The particular longhair who proposed the idea to the President would not have been disturbed by the statement that physicists in Denmark, England, France, Russia, and Germany had similar ideas at the same time and actually began to work on them.

The newspaper conception is dangerous, as well as wrong, because it gives the impression that two billion dollars can buy us anything we wish. If for two billion dollars we can buy the utilization of atomic energy and the construction of atomic bombs when none existed before, then surely for two billion dollars we can cure cancer and eradicate heart disease and other scourges. Let's go! Let's raise the money, get a director, hire the scientists, and all will be well.

We should know that all the money in the world could not have built an atomic bomb in 1936. Atomic energy was known, and many of its properties were understood. It had been released in small quantities in laboratories, and its release in large quantities in the sun and the stars had been studied. But the critical information, and the critical direction to follow for releasing it in large amounts on earth, were lacking in 1936, and no one could have used two billion dollars for making an atomic bomb at that time. It is this that is important in understanding the relation of science to industry, to medicine, and to the public. There has to be knowledge before it can be applied. At a certain stage of scientific development, theoretically critical knowledge becomes available. Before that moment—which no one can guarantee in advance—the knowledge cannot be applied. After that moment application is reasonably certain and only the special technics for its utilization need be worked out.

What is it that we learned in 1939 that we did not know in 1936? What rendered it feasible to try making an atomic bomb in 1939, the lack of which would have prevented making an atomic bomb in 1935? It was uranium fission and the associated release of neutrons. But these words are meaningless by themselves. And so too are all the other words like isotopes, Einstein's equation, protons, and plutonium that are currently found in newspaper reports.

The things and ideas for which these words stand were not discovered by the Manhattan District; they did not suddenly arrive on the scene. They arose during the continuous growth and development of a segment of science that forms one of the most fascinating chapters in the history of the human race. To extend Isaac Newton's metaphor, the development of a bomb by the release of atomic energy is merely the latest impact of the wave of physical science that began about fifty years ago on the ocean of knowledge. To understand atomic energy one must know the origin, the course, and the properties of that wave. And that means understanding the structure of the atom.

THE ATOM AS A HOMOGENEOUS BALL

1. WHY ATOMS?

When we speak of *atomic* energy and the *atomic* bomb, most of us know vaguely that these new and violent forces come from the internal structure of the atom. There we stop, because as laymen we do not even know why we assume the existence of atoms, let alone what their complicated internal workings are.

Why do we speak of atoms? Why do we say that matter is made up of a host of atoms? Objects like the table and the chair, and substances like iron and sugar, appear to be continuous. Water looks as if it were continuous, and so does the glass that contains it; otherwise the water would come through the glass.

Nevertheless, even Democritus in 400 B.C. suspected that the continuous appearance of objects and substances is not a revelation of their true structure, and he suggested that matter is basically discontinuous. He supposed it to be made up of exceedingly small parts, so small that they cannot be made any smaller. These he called atoms. Why did Democritus conceive such a curious idea?

Simple and common experience can give the answer. Ordinary table salt dissolves and disappears when put into water. So does sugar in coffee, and so do hundreds of common substances when placed in water or other liquids. If water were as continuous as it appears to be, there would be no room for the salt and sugar to disappear into. There must be holes in water; many, many holes. Moreover, salt and sugar must be made up of very tiny particles that can get into these holes and disappear.

Another experience shows this even more strikingly. Take a glass of water and put a crystal of any colored dye on the bottom. Very slowly, even without stirring, the dye dissolves and gradually spreads throughout the water. To hasten the process we stir the water and the dye, and end with an evenly colored solution in the glass. Surely both the water and the dye must be made up of microscopic particles that can mingle, so that the particles of the dye come to occupy spaces between the particles of water.

Take another common observation. A quart of water when mixed with a quart of alcohol produces less than two quarts of mixture. Part of the alcohol works its way into the spaces between the water particles, and part of the water works its way between the alcohol particles.

These things happen not only in water and other liquids. They occur in air and even in solids. Our neighbor's bacon frying in the morning liberates something that can diffuse into the air and finally reach our nostrils. Clearly there must be holes in the air, spaces where there are no air particles, so that the odoriferous fragments from the bacon can push through and reach us yards away.

If a bar of gold with a sharp clean edge is put in close contact with the similarly clean edge of a bar of silver, and the two bars are pressed together for several months and then separated, some gold can be found inside the silver bar and some silver inside the gold bar. Particles of gold and silver have migrated across the boundary. Solids can diffuse into other solids, just as gases diffuse into other gases, and solids dissolve in liquids.

All this tells us that appearance is not reality; that what we can see is only a superficial continuity of matter; that fundamentally there are innumerable holes in all substances, even the most solid. We explain these holes by supposing them to be the spaces between the ultimate small particles, the atoms, that compose matter.

2. ATOMS AND MOLECULES

The phenomena of diffusion and interpenetration are excellent reasons for assuming the existence of atoms. However, there are even better ones, and these better ones give further insight into the nature of atoms. To understand these reasons we must learn something more about the properties of matter.

It is well to start with common things like wood, bread, beans, cheese, sugar, and hair. When these materials are burned or charred they yield charcoal or carbon. Examination shows that this carbon when cleaned and purified is the same regardless of its origin. The question as to whether the carbon was in the wood and sugar all the time, or whether it was produced by the process of burning was settled long ago. We know that the carbon was there originally. Later it will be clear why.

If we now try to change the carbon by boiling it with acids, or with ammonia and other alkalis, with benzine, or with dozens of other agents, nothing happens to the carbon. It always comes back as carbon. There is almost nothing that can be done with carbon to change its appearance and properties; it remains carbon. Even if it is heated in air, and slowly disappears as a gas, the gas can be caught, and carbon can be got back from it.

Carbon is thus a substance that enters into the composition of a variety of more complex materials ranging from butter to marble; it can always be pulled out of these materials to assume its typical carbon appearance and properties; and it cannot be transformed into any simpler material. Carbon, therefore, is an irreducible, an elementary substance.

In the same way that carbon emerges from a variety of complex materials, other elementary substances such as zinc, copper, gold, sulfur, hydrogen, helium, iron, and mercury can be derived from the innumerable materials in the world. Each possesses unique properties, each differs from the other elementary substances, and each retains its individuality. No chemical procedures can transform one of these elementary substances into another. The most violent chemical actions cannot change carbon into gold, or sulfur into mercury, or lead into silver. They are irreducible elementary substances. By 1940 there were ninety-two of these substances known. They are called the chemical elements, or more briefly, elements. As one result of the atomic-bomb development, eleven more have been developed—man-made chemical elements that do not occur in nature.

All the infinite variety of materials in the world is made up of combinations of these elements, by twos, threes, fours, and even fives. Thus sugar is made of carbon, hydrogen, and oxygen; marble of calcium, carbon, and oxygen; sand of silicon and oxygen; and so on forever with the rest of the naturally occurring elements.

Since each of these elementary substances is irreducible and unique, and we have already assumed that all matter is made up of atoms, it seems sensible to suppose that the atoms that compose each element are themselves unique. In this way we can think of atoms of copper, carbon, gold, silver, hydrogen, and aluminum as special, each to its own kind. Indeed, we must assume one hundred and three different species of atoms corresponding to the as many chemical elements. The justification and the consequences of this assumption form the burden of our story, and will emerge as we develop it.

All the things on earth are made up of combinations of the chemical elements. Objects such as rocks, chairs, lampshades, and rugs are built of materials like marble, wood, iron, parchment, cotton, and wool. Some of these materials have a complicated structure of their own. Wood, for example, is not the same all through. It has grain, formed by the alternation of hard and soft fibers, and the varieties of wood depend on this visible organization. Wood is therefore an inhomogeneous substance; it cannot be purified and rendered completely homogeneous. However, the essential ingredient of wood is cellulose, which can be purified and prepared so as to be uniform throughout. Such purified, reproducible, and homogeneous materials are called pure substances, and there are hundreds of thousands of them. Sugar is one; table salt another. Aluminum, iron, calomel, bicarbonate of soda, lime, penicillin, diamond, alcohol, and DDT are examples of substances that can be prepared in pure form, so that any small fragment is like any other fragment.

When this vast array of pure substances is examined chemically, it can be divided into two kinds. First there is the small group of elementary substances like oxygen, iron, aluminum, and carbon, which we already know about. They cannot be decomposed by any chemical treatment. And second, there is the remaining, enormous group, containing substances that can be decomposed chemically to yield some of the natural elements. These pure but decomposable substances are compounded from the elements and are known as chemical compounds.

The nature of these compounds and their formation may be illustrated by the behavior of iron and sulfur. Both iron and sulfur are elements, and both are solids. If we grind them into fine powders and mix them thoroughly, they are still iron and sulfur. With a microscope the particles of sulfur and the particles of iron can be seen as separate and differently colored. If now the mixture is heated, the recurring miracle of chemistry takes place. The heated mass becomes transformed. The two separate substances disappear, and a new substance appears, made up of both iron and sulfur. This is iron sulfide, which looks, behaves, and dissolves differently from either iron or sulfur. It can be cleaned and purified, and is a compound substance uniform throughout. Iron sulfide occurs in nature as crystals, and is known as fool's gold because of its superficial resemblance to gold.

What is the ultimate structure of such compounds? They too must be built up of extremely small particles, because they too can dissolve and diffuse in liquids. In fact, our first examples of this behavior were compounds like sugar and salt. The supposition is that in compounds the ultimate particles are built up of atoms of the elements that form the compounds. In this way an atom of sulfur and an atom of iron unite to form a new unit, a molecule of iron sulfide. The smallest unit of a compound is a molecule.

Molecules are made up of atoms of one or more of the chemical elements. Because it is easy to break up compounds into their constituent elements, it must be that the atoms in the molecule maintain most of their individuality. No matter how complex the compound, no matter how large its molecule, one can always get back the constituent elements. In other words, molecules can be separated into their constituent atoms.

Until recently it could be asserted that all this talk about atoms and molecules is theory; that no one has seen an atom or a molecule, even with the highest power of the microscope. This is still true of the ordinary "light microscope"; but the electron microscope, in which light rays are replaced by a stream of electrons, provides clear pictures of at least the largest molecules, such as those of the proteins, which contain thousands of atoms, and recently a new and very simple device called the field emission microscope was invented that made it possible to see the shape of a comparatively simple molecule—that of a dye called phthalocyanin, containing less than one hundred atoms.

However, long before these first direct glimpses into the world of molecules became possible, scientists had ceased to argue as to whether these particles really existed. Atoms and molecules originated as concepts of the human mind, because they appeared useful in explaining the behavior of ordinary substances in bulk. The idea was that if we assume matter to be composed of invisible atoms or molecules, then a lot of events that are visible become understandable. The more we have learned about the properties of matter and the behavior of different substances, the more illuminating and the more reasonable appeared this relatively simple notion—that substances are made up of atoms and molecules —until it became a certainty, long before anyone saw a molecule under an electron microscope.

The procedure is something like this. We observe phenomena like diffusion, like the nontransformation of elementary substances, like the homogeneity of compounds and the ease of their decomposition into elementary substances. In order to explain these observations we assume the existence of atoms and molecules. Then we say that if atoms and molecules are what we think they are, ordinary substances should have certain definite properties that we can predict. If the predicted properties turn out to be correct, we have strengthened the reasons for believing in the reality of atoms and molecules. This reciprocal development of information and explanation is the essence of science; and in the particular field with which we are concerned, namely atomic structure, the development has been simple, logical, and frequently dramatic. When scientists finally saw direct photographs of molecules, they were thrilled, but hardly astonished, to find that, in size and shape, these particles looked exactly as they had assumed them to be.

3. THE WEIGHTS OF ATOMS

The differences between elements and compounds became clear toward the end of the eighteenth century; and in 1780 Antoine Lavoisier, the great chemist who died in the French Revolution, was able to list nearly fifty known elements. In working with elements and compounds, Lavoisier established the fundamental fact that during all the transformations of one substance into another, and of compounds into elements and the reverse, there is no loss in total weight of material involved. This is the principle of the conservation of matter. Regardless of what you do to substances, no matter how their properties change as they react with each other, no matter how different they look afterward, you end with the same total weight of matter with which you started.

As an example actually studied by Lavoisier, we can consider a burning candle. When a candle burns, it disappears and in its place gases are formed. In addition, the air surrounding the candle becomes changed so that it is no longer fit to breathe. Lavoisier knew that the hot wax of the candle combined with the oxygen of the surrounding air (which he called free air) to form water vapor and carbon dioxide (which he called fixed air). We can write this in the form of an equation as

Candle + free air = fixed air + water vapor.

Lavoisier measured the weight of the candle that disappeared and the weight of the oxygen that combined with it, and found their sum to equal the weight of the carbon dioxide and the water vapor or moisture that were formed.

In the conservation of matter during chemical reactions it makes no difference whether the beginning substances are gas or solid or liquid, and it makes no difference whether the end products are gas or solid or liquid. The important thing is to measure everything that enters into the reaction and to catch everything that forms during the reaction. If you do that, you find that there is no loss of matter. The equation balances.

The observed conservation of matter is easily translated in terms of the theoretical atoms and molecules. It says that atoms contain all the mass of any substance, and that regardless of the ways in which the atoms join to form molecules, they carry their individual masses with them. This is a revealing generalization; but the experiments that followed its formulation were even more revealing of the nature of matter. It turned out that when elements combine to form compounds they always do so in definite proportions.

For example, when you burn coal or carbon you find that by weight 3 parts of carbon always combine with 8 parts of oxygen. Thus 3 ounces of carbon as it burns take out 8 ounces of oxygen from the surrounding air. Similarly, when hydrogen in air is transformed into water vapor, the weight of oxygen consumed in the process is always eight times the weight of the hydrogen. By the same token, if you examine any pure chemical compound such as sugar, water, carbon dioxide, marble, or sulfadiazine, you always find that the elements in it exist in definite proportions by weight. From 11 pounds of carbon dioxide you can always get 3 pounds of carbon and 8 pounds of oxygen; and from 9 pounds of water you can always collect 1 pound of hydrogen and 8 pounds of oxygen.

The idea of definite proportions in the combination of elements or in the composition of compounds seems natural to us now. But it is important to put ourselves back one hundred and fifty years. At that time all that Lavoisier and the other chemists knew was that air in which a candle could burn and which was fit for breathing was rendered unfit for either job after several candles had been burned in it. The "free" air had become "fixed" air; and the chemist's problem was to find out how "fixing" air rendered it useless for burning candles and for animal breathing. It was a revelation to find that the burning candle abstracted a definite amount of material—oxygen—from the air and produced in the process a given quantity of a new substance—carbon dioxide.

The recognition of the fact that when substances combine with each other they do so in definite proportions by weight marked the emergence of chemistry as a science. It made possible the next giant step forward in understanding the nature of matter. This step was taken in 1808 by John Dalton, who formulated the modern atomic theory. The original atomic idea of Democritus was philosophically basic, but practically vague. He had suggested that matter is discontinuous and composed of indivisible atoms. Dalton started from here and built a clearly formulated, scientific, working hypothesis.

Dalton proposed the idea that an element, since it is made of atoms, has all its atoms alike. All atoms of carbon are identical; all atoms of hydrogen are identical; all atoms of iron are identical. He further suggested that the atoms of different elements differ in weight. The atom of oxygen is heavier than that of hydrogen, and the atom of iron is heavier than that of oxygen. When atoms combine with other atoms by twos or threes, they remain unchanged in the molecule, and each molecule of a compound contains a definite number of atoms. The weight of a molecule therefore is the sum of the weights of its constituent atoms. At once it is clear why when elements combine they must do so in definite proportions.

Since this is a practical scientific theory, let us see where it leads. Consider carbon dioxide. We know that when carbon and oxygen combine to form carbon dioxide, 3 parts by weight of carbon combine with 8 parts of oxygen. This is shown in Figure 1. Suppose now, that during the formation of the carbon dioxide molecule, one atom of carbon combines with two atoms of oxygen. Then together the two oxygen atoms weigh 8 units of mass compared with the carbon atom, which weighs 3 units. If two oxygen atoms weigh 8 units, then each oxygen atom must weigh 4 units compared with the carbon atom of 3 units. This ratio of 3:4 in the relative weights of carbon and oxygen can be written as 6:8 or 12:16. The reason for writing it as 12:16 will be apparent in a moment when we consider water.

Water contains by weight 1 part of hydrogen to 8 parts of oxygen. Now suppose there are two atoms of hydrogen combined with each atom of oxygen in a molecule of water. The two hydrogen atoms together therefore weigh 1 unit, and each weighs 1/2 unit. The relative weights of hydrogen

	Reaction	Carbon	+ Oxygen	= Carbon Dioxide
Fact	In Bulk (pounds)	3	+ 8	= 11
	Combining Weights	3	+ 8	= 11
Theory	Atoms	●	○○	= ○○●
	Equation	C	+ 2 O	= CO_2
	Relative weights	3	+ 2×4	= 11
	Atomic and molecular Weights	12	+ 2×16	= 44

FIGURE 1. THE BURNING OF COAL OR CARBON

When carbon and oxygen combine during the burning of coal they do so in definite proportions, weight for weight. These proportions are accounted for by the atomic theory in terms of the constituent atoms and their weights. From the behavior of matter in bulk we deduce the properties of its atoms.

and oxygen atoms must be as 1/2:8; and this ratio obviously can be written as 1:16.

Now let us set an arbitrary value of 16 units of mass as the weight of one oxygen atom. Then from these ratios it follows that the weight of a hydrogen atom is 1, and the weight of a carbon atom is 12. Notice that these relative weights of the atoms of hydrogen, carbon, and oxygen have been derived from the definite proportions by weight in which these elements in bulk combine to form carbon dioxide and water. This was part of Dalton's hypothesis. He suggested that the atoms of different elements differ in weight in the same relative way as do the combining weights of the elements when they form compounds. We have a fact and a theory. The fact is that when elements combine to form compounds they do so in definite proportions, known as their combining weights. The theory is that these relative weights are dependent on the relative weights of the atoms out of which the elements are composed.

In presenting these ideas here I have used whole numbers for the combining weights. This is not merely because it is convenient but also because it is correct as a first approximation. But only as a first approximation; and this too is of interest.

In Dalton's day the combining weights of a number of elements had been worked out with fair accuracy; and by assigning oxygen the arbitrary atomic weight of 16, the atomic weights of the known elements had been established. It is instructive to arrange the elements in the order of their atomic weights. The first twelve that were then known are·

Hydrogen	H	1.01
Lithium	Li	6.94
Beryllium	Be	9.02
Boron	B	10.82
Carbon	C	12.01
Nitrogen	N	14.01
Oxygen	O	16.00
Fluorine	F	19.00
Sodium	Na	23.00
Magnesium	Mg	24.32
Aluminum	Al	26.97
Silicon	Si	28.06

Notice in this series that, except for magnesium and boron, the atomic weights are nearly but not quite whole numbers. It is almost as if they were regular multiples of hydrogen, which has an atomic weight of practically 1. This fascination with integral multiples and whole numbers has never left the problem of atomic weights. In fact, it dominated the scene for a while when William Prout, a contemporary of Dalton, actually did suppose that all elements were made up of hydrogen. Prout's hypothesis had to be discarded because the facts persisted in showing that the atomic weights were rarely whole numbers and as a rule contained some values beyond the decimal point. We find as we go on with this story that the interest in whole numbers appears again and again as each new generalization and each new series of facts become available. Then, careful measurements show that the expected whole numbers do not materialize, and the differences between reality and expectation force us to look for new phenomena in the behavior and structure of atoms and molecules.

4. ATOMS IN SERIAL ORDER

Dalton's atomic theory was formulated at the beginning of the nineteenth century, and served as a powerful stimulus to hunt for as many elements as possible. By the middle of the century about seventy-five had been isolated and studied, and their properties had become common chemical knowledge. The first thing that became apparent was that the elements differed in atomic weight, and could be placed in serial order, much as we arranged the first twelve in the preceding section.

Another observation was that some elements were similar to others, and the similar elements seemed to occur in groups of three, called triads. The oldest and most familiar of these triads is copper, silver, and gold, whose similarities have been known for centuries. A less familiar group of three is lithium, sodium, and potassium. These are metals that are soft and shiny when freshly purified, but tarnish rapidly on exposure. In pure form all three react violently to water and therefore have to be kept immersed in kerosene. Moreover, they can be substituted for one another in compounds, and the resulting compounds are similar. Thus sodium chloride, or ordinary table salt, is white, crystalline, salty, and easily dissolved in water. So is lithium chloride, and so is potassium chloride.

Early in the nineteenth century groups of similar elements had been found only in threes, and some remnant of the medieval mystery of the number 3 hung over them. However, some of the triads were purely accidental, because all the elements were not known. As more elements were discovered and isolated, groups began to include not only three, but four, five, and sometimes six elements that behaved alike.

Such groups of similar elements were indeed tantalizing. Why should elements of such diverse atomic weights as 63.6, 107.9, and 197.2 be as similar as copper, silver, and gold? And why should two elements as similar in atomic weight as 32.1 and 35.5 be as different as sulfur and chlorine —a yellow solid and a green gas? Many were the speculations and guesses; many were the arrangements to which the elements were subjected—all to little avail until the year 1869. It was then that Dmitri I. Mendelejev, the Russian chemist, arranged the elements in a pattern known as the Periodic

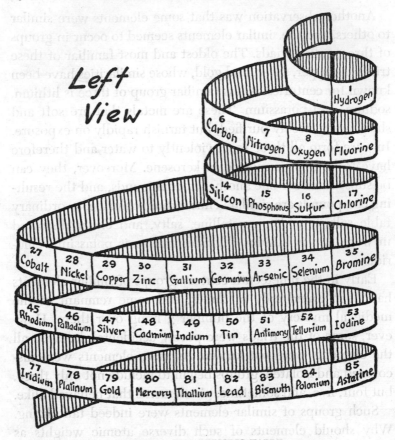

FIGURE 2. THE PERIODIC TABLE

The chemical elements have been arranged in sequence on a ribbon, and coiled in a helix. As a result, elements with similar properties fall one under the other vertically. Two views of the coiled ribbon are shown so that one can see it from both sides at the same time.

Table, which not only unified all the chemical information about them but served as well to predict the properties of undiscovered elements. Since then the Periodic Table has been the central core around which all chemical and physi-

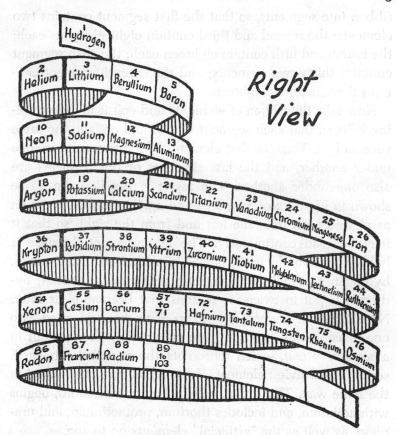

cal knowledge of the elements has grown. It has served as explanation and as inspiration, and in terms of it there has developed the beautiful edifice that is modern atomic physics and chemistry.

To construct a modern Periodic Table, write down successively along a continuous ribbon, according to their atomic numbers, the 103 elements, except for numbers 57 to 71 and 89 to 103, which should be treated as two groups, each placed in a single box. Next, draw a heavy line to divide the ribbon into segments, so that the first segment contains two elements; the second and third contain eight elements each; the fourth and fifth contain eighteen each; the sixth segment contains thirty-two elements; and the seventh segment contains the remaining eighteen.

Now take the ribbon of elements and coil it in a descending helix so that each segment begins and ends in the same vertical line. Thus the first elements of the segments are one under another, and the last elements of the segments are also one under another. The result is the Periodic Table shown in Figure 2 on pages 24 and 25. The ribbon is drawn as viewed both from the left and from the right, so that it may be read continuously. The first segment, because it holds only two elements, has to be coiled tightly. Even so, hydrogen and helium need to be separated somewhat; hydrogen is put in twice for reasons that become clear later. Note also that elements 57 to 71 have been jammed into one place as suggested on page 25; actually they jut out in a secondary coil, which represents the so-called rare-earth series. The heaviest elements, from 89 on, must be treated in the same way. This group, called the actinide series, begins with actinium, and includes thorium, protactinium, and uranium, as well as the "artificial" elements 93 to 103.

The segments of the Periodic Table contain two, eight, eighteen, or thirty-two elements. These numbers are not arbitrary; they are two times the squares of 1, 2, 3, and 4, respectively. The square of 1 is 1, which multiplied by 2 equals 2. The square of 2 is 4, which multiplied by 2 equals 8. The square of 3 is 9, which multiplied by 2 equals 18. The square of 4 is 16, which multiplied by 2 gives 32. This simple numerical series was not known to Mendelejev; we learn more about it later.

A host of interesting relations becomes evident in the Periodic Table. The first segment-coil begins with hydrogen and ends with helium, which is an inert gas. The next segment-coil begins with lithium, the soft metal we have already discussed, and ends with neon, another inert gas, used in illuminated signs. The third coil begins with sodium, a metal like lithium, and ends with argon, another inert gas, also used in signs. The fourth coil begins with potassium, another of the soft metals, takes in more elements than the preceding coil, and ends with krypton, which is still another inert gas, much like helium, neon, and argon. The fifth segment begins with rubidium, which, like sodium and potassium, is a soft metal, and ends with xenon, a gas like neon and helium. In short, all the elements in the first vertical column are similar, and all the elements in the terminal column are similar.

Precisely the same is true of the other vertical columns, even the short ones. Note our old friends the triad of copper, silver, and gold under element 29. Or take the elements next to these: zinc, cadmium, and mercury, which form a triad of similar metals known from the days of the alchemists. Now skip to the column formed by the penultimate elements of each coil: fluorine, chlorine, bromine, and iodine. Even the most uninitiated knows that the first three are noxious gases and that iodine easily becomes a smelly gas at ordinary temperature.

Perhaps the most curious series of elements is in the vertical column under helium. All are gases, and all were unknown and even unsuspected at the time of Mendelejev. They were discovered after 1890 by Lord Rayleigh and William Ramsay. With the exception of radon they occur normally in the air in very minute amounts. They are called "noble gases" because with few exceptions they do not combine with other elements; they act as if they are quite satisfied with themselves. Most other elements combine relatively easily with others. The noble gases stand at the end of each coil, one under another.

When Mendelejev first arranged the Periodic Table only about seventy-five elements were known. Therefore it was not so easy to see the regularities as it is now. Many empty spaces had to be put in, and it required an original feat of creative imagination to arrange the available elements in this regular and intelligible series. Mendelejev, however, did more than this. He had the intellectual courage to predict not merely the existence of these missing elements but also their quantitative properties. In every instance his predictions were verified, with remarkable accuracy.

As an example of this prediction, consider spot 32 in the fourth horizontal coil of the Periodic Table. This element lies in the vertical column between silicon and tin, and is now called germanium. Mendelejev in 1871 predicted its existence and called it eka-silicon. He said it would be grayish-white in color, and would give a white oxide when burned in air, and would not be affected by acids or by alkalis. Moreover, he gave definite values for its atomic weight, its density, its atomic volume, and even its boiling point. Fifteen years later, when Clemens Winkler discovered and isolated it, he found Mendelejev's predictions almost perfectly fulfilled. Winkler called the element germanium for obvious national reasons, as is commonly done.

Prediction always appears mysterious. But quantitative prediction of the properties of unknown things appears doubly mysterious. Sometimes the process is relatively easy and obvious; sometimes it involves a kind of inspired guessing that only a person of considerable scientific experience can do. In the present case it depends on the fact that the properties of the elements are periodic; similar properties occur at regular intervals when the elements are arranged in the order of atomic weights.

As a simple example, suppose that one of the elements in the vertical column under lithium were not known. One could say in advance that it must be a soft metal since all the others in that column are like that. One could also say that it must be an alkali metal, which does not exist free in the natural state, because it is easily changed in the air and reacts violently with water. These are the properties of lithium, sodium, potassium, rubidium, and cesium. Therefore, if one of these were missing, as francium was until recently, its obvious properties could be predicted.

The more detailed and quantitative predictions require closer study. Figure 3 shows the relation that various elements have to a property known as the atomic volume, which is the volume or space occupied by an element as a solid in an amount of grams (1/28 ounce) equal to its atomic weight. Thus the atomic volume is the volume taken up by 6.94 grams of lithium, 9.02 grams of beryllium, 12.01 grams of carbon, and so on. From the drawing it is apparent that this property goes through cycles as the elements increase in atomic weight. The maximal atomic volume in each cycle is attained by the metals of the column in the Periodic Table under lithium, and includes sodium, potassium, rubidium, and cesium. The values for the other elements lie on the slopes and valleys between these peaks. Obviously, after the atomic weight of an unknown element has been estimated, it is easy to calculate its probable atomic volume merely by picking its position on the periodic graph (Figure 3).

When Mendelejev made the Periodic Table there were many empty spaces in it. He was able to construct the table in the order of atomic weights.

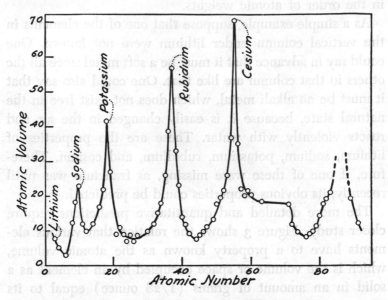

FIGURE 3. ATOMIC VOLUME AND ATOMIC NUMBER

Notice the regular way in which the atomic volume rises and falls as the elements grow heavier; notice also how the soft alkali metals all lie on the peaks, while the other elements fall in between.

only by putting similar elements into the same vertical columns. All the empty spaces have now been filled, and the elements can be arranged in succession from 1 to 99 as we have done. This numbering of the elements in sequence has turned out to be a property even more useful than the atomic weight. Each element thus has an atomic number recording its location in the sequence from hydrogen to uranium. The Periodic Table then shows that elements with similar characteristics occur at regular intervals of two, eight, eighteen, or thirty-two elements apart.

It is tempting to ask what these numbers mean and what this periodicity tells us. They must surely be an expression of the internal structure of the atom. However, even at the

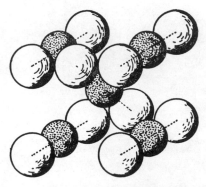

FIGURE 4. A CRYSTAL OF SOLID CARBON DIOXIDE, OR DRY ICE

Notice how each carbon atom (stippled) always has two oxygen atoms attached to it. A large crystal contains millions of such units arranged in this orderly geometrical way.

end of the nineteenth century no one knew anything about the inside of atoms. When a chemist or a physicist thought of an atom he considered it a solid sphere like a billiard ball, relatively hard and uniform throughout.

Even now this concept of an atom is useful for most work in chemistry. The organic chemist who builds complicated molecules like those of DDT or penicillin or rubber rarely thinks of the atom in any other way. The mineralogist still uses this concept whenever he wishes to describe the crystal structure of a compound. Figure 4 is an example of a kind of diagram that is repeatedly employed to make visual the make-up of chemical compounds. It is a diagram of solid carbon dioxide. The arrangement of the atoms in the molecule accounts for the properties of the compounds.

II

THE ATOM BECOMES COMPLEX

1. THE SURFACE OF ATOMS

Even before the end of the nineteenth century many chemists knew that the concept of the atom as a homogeneous elastic ball was merely a useful fiction. It explained a tremendous amount about the structure of matter, but it could not be true. There were several reasons for this, and the investigation of the reasons furnished new information that helped clarify and expand our ideas about atoms.

The most potent doubt about the complete homogeneity of atoms comes from the fact that atoms join with each other to form molecules. Billiard balls do not stick to each other, or enter into stable combinations by twos and threes. But atoms do; and because they combine, their surfaces must have special arrangements for holding on tightly to one another. Chemists called these holding devices bonds; and they soon found consistent regularities in the number and strength of the bonds that different elements possess.

An atomic bond can be defined as the capacity of an atom to hold a hydrogen atom or its equivalent. For example, an oxygen atom can hold two hydrogen atoms as in H_2O, water; therefore it has two bonds. A carbon atom can hold four hydrogen atoms as in methane, CH_4, and therefore it has four bonds. Moreover, since each oxygen atom has two

33

bonds, carbon can hold two oxygen atoms, as in carbon dioxide, which is CO_2. A nitrogen atom can hold three hydrogen atoms as in ammonia, NH_3, and therefore has three bonds.

Elements in the same vertical column of the Periodic Table have the same number of atomic bonds. Often these bonds are spoken of as valences, especially when the elements rather than their atoms are referred to. In this way, hydrogen is single valent, or monovalent; oxygen is divalent; nitrogen, trivalent; and carbon, tetravalent.

All chemical reactions consist of the transformation of one molecular species into another, or several others. For example, when wood burns, the complex molecule of cellulose, which contains atoms of carbon, hydrogen, and oxygen, is transformed by combination with more oxygen atoms from the air into molecules of water and carbon dioxide. By means of their bonds the atoms in molecules can be rearranged into new combinations of atoms to produce different molecules.

Some bonds are tighter than others. The tighter they are, the more stable are the compounds. The looser the bonds, the less stable are the compounds and the more likely they are to break apart with the release of energy. Thus when atoms change their affiliations with other atoms the process may require energy or it may give off energy, depending on the stability of the initial and final products. Therefore some chemical reactions will take place only with the addition of energy in the form of heat, light, or electricity, while other reactions give off heat, light, or electricity.

Ultimately all the energy we use comes from the light of the sun. Green plants absorb this light and use it as energy with which to build up compounds of carbon, hydrogen, and oxygen. The carbon-hydrogen combination involves bonds that are loose, and it is therefore particularly high in energy. It is present in gasoline, sugar, starch, wood, and the like, and when these are used as fuels the carbon-hydrogen combination is replaced by a carbon-oxygen combination that is tighter, and therefore much lower in energy. At the same time, the very loose bonds combining two oxygen atoms in an oxygen molecule are replaced by the extremely stable oxygen-hydrogen bonds in water. The difference in energy between the bond combinations before and after the reaction is given off and furnishes us with motor power and heat.

Even explosives like TNT act only by the energy released by their bonds in the rearrangement of their component elements. When TNT explodes, its large molecule is first broken into small molecules like carbon dioxide, water vapor, and nitrogen gas, which contain much less energy in their bond combinations than did the original molecule. The difference in energy is released as heat, which acts on these gases to expand them suddenly. It is this sudden expansion that is the explosion.

What are these surface structures, these bonds? Obviously a bond is not a hook that one atom sticks into another. If this were so, there would be aggressive atoms and passive atoms, and there is no evidence for this. The behavior of the elements is such that, in water for example, it is just as correct to say that one oxygen atom holds two hydrogen atoms as that two hydrogen atoms hold one oxygen atom between them. Bonds represent reciprocal arrangements between atoms. When two atoms are joined, each atom undoubtedly contributes something to the bond holding them together.

But what is this that each atom contributes to make the bond that ties it to another atom? For years no one knew.

Chemists generally were satisfied with the idea of bonds without caring much about its ultimate meaning. In fact, the answer to the question came not from chemistry but from electricity. And when the answer came it far transcended the original question, because it helped our understanding of many other phenomena besides atomic structure.

2. ELECTRONS FROM THE SURFACE OF ATOMS

The ancient Greeks knew that when an amber rod is rubbed with wool or fur, the amber becomes electrically charged, and is capable of picking up bits of straw and paper. Similarly, glass rods and many other objects when they are rubbed with silk, wool, or fur become electrified. Some substances become positively charged, whereas others become negatively charged; this classification depends on whether in the charged state they are attracted or repelled by charged amber, which is arbitrarily considered negative. The Greek word for amber is *elektron.*

This kind of electrification of objects was called static or frictional electricity, and for many years it was considered different from flowing electricity, which had been discovered by Luigi Galvani and by Alessandro Volta in the eighteenth century. Flowing electricity is the form we know commonly; it is easily made chemically from batteries and flows along wires. However, one of the accomplishments of the nineteenth century was to show that the two sorts of electricity are really the same. The experiments for this purpose involved the discovery and isolation of the fundamental unit of electricity—the electron.

Let us take a glass tube sealed at each end, with a metal plate inside each end connected by a wire to an outside source of current. Such a system is shown in Figure 5. When the current is turned on, nothing happens in the tube. Normally the air in the tube offers such resistance to the passage of electricity that no current flows through it. If, however, the air has previously been sucked out of the tube so that the inside is almost a vacuum, the electricity can jump across

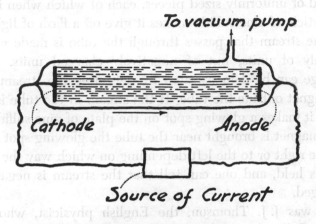

FIGURE 5. A GEISSLER TUBE

As the current is passed through the near vacuum in the tube, a stream of negative electrons passes from the negative cathode to the positive anode. The extremely dilute gas in the tube shows all sorts of pretty colors during the passage of the current.

the long gap in the tube, between the two terminal metal plates.

When the current jumps from one metal plate to the other, something actually passes through the gas in the tube; something flows in a stream from one end to the other. If a small glass plate coated with zinc sulfide is placed in the path of the stream inside the tube, the zinc sulfide lights up the moment the current is turned on. If you look closely at the glowing plate of zinc sulfide, you can see that the glow is made up of tiny bursts of light all over it. It is as if now one particle of zinc sulfide is hit and bursts into a flash of light, then another particle of zinc sulfide is hit and bursts into light, then another, and another, and so on. The bursts of light are all the same size, a phenomenon that shows that the stream of electricity passing through the tube is composed of uniformly sized pieces, each of which when it hits a particle of zinc sulfide makes it give off a flash of light.

The stream that passes through the tube is made up not merely of units, but of negatively charged units. Their charge can be demonstrated by deflecting the stream with a magnet outside the tube. If the stream in the tube is narrow, it makes a glowing spot on the plate of zinc sulfide. As the magnet is brought near the tube the glowing spot shifts to the right or to the left depending on which way the magnet is held, and one can tell that the stream is negatively charged.

It was J. J. Thomson, the English physicist, who first showed that this stream is made up of charged unit particles, and he succeeded in weighing them. This sounds mysterious, but it is not. Just remember that it is easier to deflect a moving stream of ping-pong balls than a moving stream of freight cars. When a moving object is heavy it takes a lot of force to pull it out of its direct path, whereas if it is light, it can easily be pushed or pulled out of its motion in a straight line.

By measuring the magnetic force required to divert the stream of charged particles in the evacuated tube, J. J. Thomson was able to measure their mass. They turned out to be lighter by far than anything previously known. It will be recalled that the hydrogen atom was the lightest previously known material particle. Each of these charged units weighs only 1/1840 as much as a hydrogen atom.

As a result of this work we possess a new unit of matter, a particle that is 1840 times lighter than a hydrogen atom, and, unlike the hydrogen atom, carries a unit charge of electricity. In fact, Thomson was able to show that it *is* a unit charge of electricity. He called these new particles electrons, and demonstrated that they form the electric current. Electricity is electrons, and when the current flows, electrons move.

All electrons are alike. In Figure 5 the electrons come out of the metal plate on the left called the cathode, and travel to the metal plate on the right called the anode. It makes no difference what these metals are; the electrons that stream out from the negative cathode are all alike. They all weigh the same, and all have the same electrical charge.

Where are the electrons when the current does not flow through the evacuated tube? Where are the electrons in the battery when the wires are not connected? Where are the electrons when the generator is not turning in the power-house? These questions bring us right back to the structure of atoms. Clearly the electrons must be somewhere, since surely they are not created the moment the switch is closed in the lighting circuit. Where are they?

The electrons are in ordinary matter. Consider frictional electricity. The amber that has been rubbed with fur is negatively charged. This means that the amber has acquired electrons on its surface. These electrons can be led off the surface by a conducting wire and properly measured. They are the same electrons that form the stream in the evacuated tube and the current in the electric light. The amber acquired these electrons from the fur by rubbing them off the fur. As a result the amber became negative and the fur positive.

Evidently it is fairly easy to rub electrons off many materials. We do this every time we walk briskly on a carpet.

The electrons are pulled off the carpet material and accumulate on the surface of the body. When we touch something metallic that can conduct the electrons from the surface of the body to the ever-receptive earth, they jump as a spark across the point of contact, and it is this concentration of electrons that causes the shock we feel on such occasions.

By various means electrons can be pulled out of all sorts of objects, no matter how innocent-looking. Fur, carpets, copper, gold, cheese, salt, and even water yield electrons. Electrons can be boiled off a wire merely by heating it in a vacuum, as happens in every vacuum tube in a radio set. Some of these electrons must be near the surface of the matter from which they can be rubbed off so easily. And since all matter is made of atoms, some of the electrons must be near or on the surface of the atoms.

Ordinarily, objects are electrically neutral, and so are their atoms. When their surface electrons are pulled off, objects and their constituent atoms become positively charged, while the substance acquiring the electrons becomes negatively charged. It looks as if atoms in their normal or neutral condition are made of something positive, combined with electrons, which are negative. Atoms cannot be considered any longer as uniform homogeneous elastic balls. They have a structure; and at least the surface of this structure is concerned with the way in which atoms stick together to form molecules.

In the last section we learned that when two atoms are joined, each contributes something to the bonds that hold them together. Without going into the details of the experiments, we can say at once that what each atom contributes to the bond is an electron. The chemical bond that keeps atoms together consists of a pair of electrons, one from each atom, which the participating atoms hold in common. In this way a one-bond atom (a monovalent atom) like hydrogen, or sodium, has one surface electron ready to be shared with another atom that is capable of reciprocal action.

The result is a two-electron tie that keeps the atoms together. Elements that are divalent have two surface electrons that can be shared, and these can be reciprocally taken up by another divalent atom or by two monovalent atoms. And so on with trivalent atoms.

Water has the capacity of breaking some of these bonds in such a way that one atom gives up its electron and becomes positive, while the other atom takes up the electron and becomes negative. For example, the gas hydrochloric acid consists of neutral molecules HCl. When it is dissolved in water, each hydrogen atom acquires an electron and becomes H^+ (positive hydrogen ion), while each chlorine atom becomes Cl^- (negative chlorine ion). Both ions become surrounded by water molecules attracted by their charges. A crystal of sodium chloride, NaCl, reacts similarly in water.

If a current of electricity is sent through such a salt solution, Na^+ picks up a negative charge at the cathode or negative pole, and becomes a neutral sodium atom (which reacts with water to form sodium hydroxide, NaOH). We can measure the number of electrons (the amount of current) required to discharge a certain large number of sodium atoms at the cathode. Let us call this amount a faraday of electricity. We can also measure the current that is required to discharge that same number of copper atoms out of solution. The result is two faradays of electricity. Thus it takes twice as many electrons to form a neutral copper atom as it did to make a sodium atom. In other words, in solution copper was Cu^{++} while sodium was Na^+. Copper is divalent, and sodium is monovalent. And this holds not only here but in all the chemical transformations that sodium and copper undergo. In the same way we find that aluminum, which is trivalent, requires three electrons to be neutralized and deposited out of solution. In solution it is therefore Al^{+++}.

A substance in the charged condition such as Na^+ or Cu^{++} or Cl^- is often spoken of as ionized, and the individual charged atoms like Al^{+++} are called ions. The Greek word *ion* means wanderer, and these charged atoms are so called because they can wander in an electric field.

Gone now is the simple billiard-ball atom. In its place we have a sort of electrically neutral structure with easily detachable electrons on the surface. By the end of the nineteenth century this was all that was known for sure. However, during the last five years of the century there were ominous rumblings of future transformations in this simple structure that would eventually lead to the atomic bomb. These rumblings were the discoveries of X rays and radioactivity.

3. RAYS FROM THE INTERIOR OF ATOMS

In describing the discovery of electrons I pictured what happens in an evacuated glass tube with sealed-in metal electrodes. Such tubes are tricky to make. The metal plates inside have to be connected with an outside source of electricity by means of wires that pass through the glass, and it is hard to make the joint of wire and glass airtight. In Germany there was an excellent glass blower by the name of Heinrich Geissler who learned the trick of sealing wires in a glass tube so that the seal remained tight even when the tube itself was almost completely exhausted of air. For this reason the tubes were known as Geissler tubes.

It was in such a Geissler tube that J. J. Thomson discovered electrons and measured their mass and charge. The stream of electrons in the Geissler tube could be made visible by their impact on a fluorescent zinc sulfide screen, and one could almost count the individual electron impacts as they produced bursts of light in the zinc sulfide particles of the screen.

The discharges through Geissler tubes are rather pretty, and served as items in the repertory of the physics professor to interest students and keep them awake. Many people had become familiar with them toward the end of the last century, but up to 1895 all attention had been concentrated on the effects produced inside the tube by the stream of electrons, or cathode rays, as they were then called. One looked at the glass, or at the anode plate, or at the fluorescent screen near the anode.

It was in 1895 that the German physicist Wilhelm K. Roentgen discovered that something comes off the anode through the glass and is scattered all around it. He found this phenomenon because he noticed that even when the Geissler tube was completely covered by black paper, a fluorescent zinc-sulfide screen held outside near the Geissler tube in the dark glowed when the tube was discharged. Roentgen observed that the fluorescence was strongest just near the anode, and he concluded that something was given off by the anode that could penetrate glass and paper and affect the zinc sulfide.

Roentgen called the things that were given off X rays because they acted like rays of light, but were not light, and their nature was unknown. They were not electrons because electrons cannot pass through glass or paper, and these passed easily through both.

We know now that X rays are really much like rays of light, but of shorter wavelength, and more penetrating power. Ordinary light is made up of a series of waves. So are X rays. The difference is that the X-ray waves are extremely short in comparison. The precise wavelength depends on the voltage of the current going through the Geissler tube.

One hardly needs to spend time describing X rays, because almost everybody knows about them these days. From the plaything of the physicists, they have become the great tools of medical diagnosis and treatment. The types, sizes, shapes, and powers of X-ray tubes depend upon the purposes for which they are needed, from the small model used by the dentist to the enormously powerful instruments used in the treatment of cancer.

For our present story, X rays are important because they demand an explanation. Evidently they are emitted from the metal of the anode when it is struck by the electrons in the Geissler tube. What produces them, and where do they come from? They must come from the atoms of the metal when these are hit by electrons in motion. But how and why? Before it was possible to formulate an answer, the scientific world was presented with an even greater mystery by the discovery of radioactivity.

4. ENERGY FROM THE INTERIOR OF ATOMS

Roentgen had discovered X rays by the glow or fluorescence of a zinc-sulfide screen. Many other substances besides zinc sulfide fluoresce, and the properties and classification of such materials were a specialty of the physicist Henri

Becquerel. In fact, they had been a specialty of his father before him.

Some minerals when quickly brought into the dark after exposure to light can be seen to glow for some time afterward. Experiments showed that sunlight was most effective in producing this "phosphorescence," and that it was the invisible ultraviolet light that actually did the work. An electric mercury-vapor arc in an ultraviolet-transparent glass or quartz vessel is even more effective. The minerals absorb the invisible ultraviolet light and emit ordinary visible light at once and later.

One story has it that Becquerel wondered whether, in addition to the ordinary visible light that they emit on exposure to the sun, such minerals may not also produce invisible light and perhaps even more penetrating rays, like those just discovered by Roentgen. He therefore placed some of the minerals in a tray on top of a carefully wrapped photographic plate, and exposed the arrangement to the sunlight. His idea was that if invisible or active rays were emitted as fluorescence they would penetrate the black paper and fog the photographic plate. And sure enough, the plate did show considerable fogging with some of the minerals.

However, this was not the end. The story continues that the sun did not shine every day in that winter of 1896 in Paris, and Becquerel, after setting up the mineral in the tray on the wrapped photographic plate, placed the whole preparation in a drawer in his laboratory to wait for the sun. The sun did not shine for a few days, and he therefore used the photographic plate for some other purpose. On developing it, he was astonished to find it badly fogged, much as if it had been under the fluorescent mineral that was being exposed to sunlight. Evidently even in the dark and without previous exposure to sunlight, the mineral had given off some rays that had passed right through the paper and affected the photographic plate.

A survey showed that a number of minerals had this strange property. Further study revealed that only those minerals that contained the element uranium were capable of spontaneously giving off this invisible penetrating radiation, and that the extent of fogging of the photographic plate was proportional to the uranium content of the mineral. Becquerel called these minerals "radioactive" because of their capacity to give off this extraordinary radiation.

One of Becquerel's colleagues was Pierre Curie, who with his wife Marie became interested in these phenomena. Becquerel suggested that Marie Curie study for this penetrating radiation as large a variety of minerals as possible. In so doing, she found that there was one other element in addition to uranium that could produce radioactivity. This element was thorium, and Marie Curie and her husband Pierre were soon able to show that the capacity to fog a photographic plate in the dark was proportional to the uranium or thorium content of the mineral, depending on which it contained.

With one exception. This was the black mineral pitchblende, which though it contained uranium, showed a radioactivity much more powerful than could be accounted for by its uranium content. The Curies suspected that there might be still another radioactive element besides uranium and thorium. If this were true, the unknown element would have to be much more powerful than uranium, because pitchblende is mostly uranium, and only a trifling percentage of this unknown and undetected element would have to be responsible for the exceptional power of pitchblende to blacken a photographic plate kept in the dark.

The rest of this tale is not for us to tell here; it has already been reported in books, movies, and the press, and has become common knowledge of our time. The Curies worked at the problem for a number of years and by their efforts discovered the new element that they had suspected. That new element was radium.

Radium and radioactivity were not easily assimilated by physicists at the end of the nineteenth century. Henry Adams records that S. P. Langley, the physicist of the Smithsonian Institution, was deeply troubled as he looked at the radium and radioactivity demonstration at the Paris Exposition of 1900. Here are elements that without any outside supply of energy keep on steadily emitting powerful and penetrating rays. Where do these rays come from? Clearly they must come from the atoms of uranium, thorium, and radium. But if so, what sort of structures can these atoms be? Certainly they cannot be the old homogeneous balls; they must have structures deep inside that can emit these rays of enormous penetrating power without themselves changing perceptibly.

5. FRAGMENTS FROM THE INTERIOR OF ATOMS

With the study of radium and radioactivity we enter the twentieth century. Much of the chemical work on radium and its related compounds was done by the Curies, and for that they and Becquerel were awarded a Nobel Prize in 1903. However, it is the physical aspects of radioactivity that are of interest in the development of our story. These investigations were made by several people, but especially by the British physicist Ernest Rutherford in Montreal, then in Manchester, and later in Cambridge, England.

The basic phenomenon is that a covered photographic plate held near radium becomes blackened on subsequent development, as if it had been struck by light. Similarly a glass plate covered with zinc sulfide glows when it is brought near radium in the dark. This principle is used in making luminous dials on watches. Radium paint is zinc sulfide plus a trace of radium, which keeps the zinc sulfide aglow. A zinc-sulfide plate and a photographic plate are two devices used in exploring the nature of what is given off by radium.

Figure 6 illustrates the kind of experiments that were made for this purpose. Radium has to be kept in lead containers, because what it gives off is injurious to life. Imagine a long and narrow tube of lead with one end sealed, and with a few grains of radium at the bottom. The reason for the long narrow tube is that whatever is given off by the radium has to travel along the length of the tube, and will come out in a narrow beam traveling in a straight line. One can explore the shape and character of this beam by placing a photographic plate at different distances from the opening and seeing what size spots are produced. Easier still is using a zinc-sulfide screen. Placed near the opening of the lead tube, the screen glows in a small circle the diameter of the opening. As the screen is moved away from the opening the circle increases very slightly, which shows that the beam is straight and well defined, but very slightly divergent.

Now bring a strong magnet near the beam, and observe what happens to the fluorescent circle. It is still there, but it has become distinctly weaker. This change means that there is still a beam that goes straight out, undeflected as before, but it has become less intense. By exploring with our fluorescent screen the region around the opening we can find out what has happened to weaken our beam. Instead of one circular spot, we can now find three, the central one and one on each side. Remove the magnet, and all three jump together to form the undeviated central beam; return the magnet and the beam splits into three. Evidently, at least three different rays are given off by the radium. Rutherford called these "alpha," "beta," and "gamma" rays.

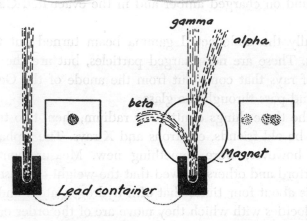

FIGURE 6. RAYS FROM RADIUM

In the drawing to the left, all the rays leave the container in one beam, which shows as a glowing circular spot on the plate of zinc sulfide. In the drawing to the right, a magnet is held perpendicular to the plane of the page. At once the beam breaks into three parts: the alpha beam to the right, the beta to the left, and the undeflected gamma beam straight ahead. These are shown as three glowing circles on the zinc-sulfide plate.

Further examination revealed the nature of the three kinds of rays. The alpha ray was deflected by the magnet in such a way as to show that it was positively charged. Moreover, it was only slightly deflected even by a powerful magnet. Therefore, it was probably composed of relatively heavy, charged particles. These were named alpha particles.

Toward the other side of the undeflected beam was the

beta ray. It was easily deflected by the magnet in such a way as to show that it was negatively charged. Moreover, it was deflected much more than the alpha beam; therefore its negatively charged particles were much lighter than the alpha particles. These negative beta particles were easy to identify: they were electrons, the same kind of electrons that are found on charged amber and in the evacuated Geissler tubes.

Finally the undeflected gamma beam turned out to be X rays. These are not charged particles, but are the same kind of rays that come out from the anode of the Geissler tube and pass through the glass.

Of the three things emitted by radium, then, two turned out to be old friends, electrons and X rays. The alpha particles, however, were something new. Measurements by Rutherford and others showed that the weight of these particles is about four times that of a hydrogen atom and that the velocities with which they move are of the order of one-tenth the speed of light. What are they? The inert gas helium has an atomic weight of 4, which means that its atom weighs four times as much as a hydrogen atom. One might therefore guess the identity of an alpha particle. But please remember that helium is a noble gas and was not well known in 1900. It was not until later that the alpha particle was shown to be an ionized helium atom, an atom of helium from which two electrons had been stripped off, and which is therefore He^{++}.

In addition to these three rays, it was soon found that around radium or minerals containing radium the air becomes a good conductor of electricity. A conductor of electricity is something that permits electricity to go from one spot to another. This passage of electricity takes place when the intervening atoms become charged or ionized. Something was being given off that ionized the air around the radium. And furthermore, a certain amount of heat was steadily generated.

Radium gives off all these things all the time. And no outside influence—not light nor heat nor electricity—has any effect on the rate with which radium emits these radiations and particles. These emissions from radium involve the release of tremendous energies. An alpha particle travels very fast indeed and therefore has lots of energy. The beta particles, which are electrons, also travel fast. Since they are so much smaller than alpha particles they do not involve so much energy, but there is energy aplenty. And then there are the X rays and the heat.

All this goes on indefinitely, day in and day out, year in and year out. The energy that drives out these electrons and alpha particles and gamma rays and heat must come from somewhere. The alpha particles and the electrons themselves must also come from somewhere. They can come only from the interior of the atom, not from its surface. The rearrangement of atoms in molecules could never yield energies or particles of this magnitude. Heretofore all the energies that were known came from the changing of the bonds between atoms in the molecules of compounds. These were the chemical energies that served for fire, fuel, and explosives. With radioactivity, energies were being released that were of a totally different order of magnitude from those furnished by chemical transformations.

For example, measurements even on minute amounts of radium showed that if 1 ounce of radium were to deliver all the X rays, alpha particles, and electrons of which it is capable, the energy would be equivalent to the heat supplied by 10 tons of coal. Ten tons of coal are roughly 320,000 ounces, which means that weight for weight radium can yield 320,000 times as much energy as coal.

Such measurements and computations were made very early in the century. Moreover, the energy released was spoken of as atomic (or, more correctly, nuclear) energy. It is well to keep this in mind as an antidote to the not uncommon notion that atomic energy was suddenly discovered as a great secret just before World War II. To scientists atomic energy is an old story. It was forty years old when the first atom bomb was exploded.

III

THE ATOM DEVELOPS A STRUCTURE

1. THE ATOM HAS A NUCLEUS   RAD = He++

During its existence radium continues to emit alpha particles, which we found to be helium stripped of two electrons. What is left of the radium after it has given off these alpha particles? The answer came when it was observed that around the radium there accumulates a strange gas. This gas was called radium emanation because no one quite knew what it was. Later its properties were studied, and we now know that it is a gas like neon and krypton, a member of the group of noble gases that are in the terminal column of the Periodic Table. When its identity became established radium emanation was named radon, a combination of the first and last few letters of its original designation.

What should this gas be? Marie Curie found that the atomic weight of radium is nearly 226. If each radium atom emits an alpha particle that has an atomic weight of 4, and if what is left becomes the gas radon, then it should have an atomic weight of 222. It took some time to accumulate enough radon gas for the British chemist William Ramsay to determine its atomic weight. And it was exciting to learn that its atomic weight is really 222. This information tells us either that helium is suddenly created out of radium, or more likely, that the atom of radium is an arrangement from which the helium particle can be easily formed or detached. In either case the radium atom must have a structure of some complexity.

It was Rutherford who performed the experiments that defined this structure. The alpha particle turned out to be most useful in these experiments because it was a particle with two positive charges and a mass of 4 that could be sent in a stream moving with great velocities. In air such a stream of alpha particles, as it issues from radium, goes about 5 or 6 inches before it is dissipated by contact with the millions of atoms that it meets. Rutherford directed the alpha particles close against a thin piece of gold leaf and by means of the fluorescent zinc-sulfide screen he watched what happened to the beam of particles.

Three things occurred, which are shown in Figure 7. First, most of the alpha particles by far breezed right through the gold leaf as if it were not there. This seemed to show that so far as the alpha particle is concerned, gold leaf is mostly empty space. Second, some of the alpha particles were slightly deflected from their straight path. And third, an occasional alpha particle bounced back or was sharply deflected as if it had hit something its own size. The relative infrequency of such a direct collision emphasizes the fact that the gold leaf is mainly vacant space. Considering that the alpha particle is a helium atom, that gold is a solid with its atoms packed close together, and that gold is a relatively heavy atom, this emptiness of the gold leaf is much greater than can be accounted for by the comparatively small spaces between the gold atoms. It must be that the gold atom itself contains a lot of empty space.

Once this was recognized it became necessary to devise a new picture of the atom, a picture that would account for not only all the old chemical knowledge but the new radio-activity information as well. It was Rutherford who supplied this new picture. He suggested that the atom is made of two parts—a tiny central nucleus in which most of the mass is concentrated, and the rest of the atom, with a diameter about ten thousand times as large as the nucleus. This region around the nucleus is space containing electrons. Electrons

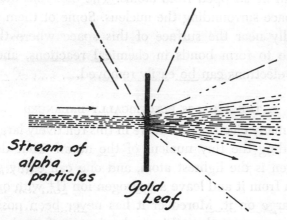

Stream of alpha particles

Gold Leaf

FIGURE 7. STREAM OF ALPHA PARTICLES THROUGH GOLD LEAF
Note that, whereas most of the particles go straight through, some are slightly deflected and others are bounced back at sharp angles as if they had hit something hard.

are negative, and since the atom as a whole is neutral, the nucleus must be positive.

In these terms an alpha particle is really only the tiny nucleus of a helium atom, because its two electrons have been stripped off. Since it is so minute, it can sweep through gold leaf without meeting anything. Mostly it goes through the empty region around the nucleus of the gold atom. This idea also explains why every once in a while when an alpha particle hits the nucleus of a gold atom it bounces back or is sharply deflected. The reason is that the gold nucleus is positively charged and the alpha particle is positively charged and they both contain the major mass of the atom. They are both tiny and therefore meet only rarely; but when they do collide the result is a really massive encounter, which sets the lighter alpha particle bouncing back across space. Finally, the idea explains the relative ease with which electrons can be stripped from atoms. The electrons are in the large space surrounding the nucleus. Some of them are undoubtedly near the surface of this space where they are available to form bonds in chemical reactions, and these surface electrons can be easily removed.

2. THE ATOM IS ELECTRICALLY BALANCED

How many electrons are there in this relatively large space surrounding the tiny nucleus of the atom? That depends. Hydrogen is the lightest atom, and one can easily strip an electron from it and leave a hydrogen ion H^+ with one positive charge on it. Moreover it has never been possible to remove any more than this single electron from hydrogen.

Perhaps there is only one electron in hydrogen. Let us suppose so for a moment. Then the hydrogen atom whose weight is 1 would be made up of (a) a nucleus whose weight is also 1 with a single positive charge on it, and (b) one electron with its mass of $1/1840$ and its single negative charge roaming in the space around the nucleus.

Helium is the next element in order, with an atomic weight of 4. It is relatively easy to strip one electron from helium, and not too difficult to remove a second electron as well, leaving ionized He^{++}. These are the alpha particles that come roaring out of radium with velocities of 18,000 miles per second; but similar particles can be produced in the laboratory by sending an electric current through a Geissler tube with a little helium in it. Since no more electrons can be pulled out, it seems entirely possible that the helium atom really has only two electrons in the space around the nucleus. The nucleus would then be left with a mass of 4 and with two positive charges on it to balance the two negative electrons around it.

Is it possible that the third element, lithium, has three electrons; the fourth element, beryllium, four electrons; the fifth, boron, five electrons; and so on to uranium, which might have ninety-two electrons? It is not only possible; it is true. The evidence for this regular augmentation in the number of electrons as one goes from one element to the next in the Periodic Table is varied and plentiful. Some of it is amusing, and shows how work in one field, even if only by analogy, can enrich the knowledge of another field.

When a beam of sunlight enters a darkened room with dust in it, one can see the beam of light clearly defined as the light is scattered from the dust particles. The more dust particles in the room the more the light is scattered; and if there is a real cloud of dust, the light is scattered so much that one can hardly see beyond it. The same thing happens to the beams from the headlights of a car in a fog. The small particles of water making up the fog in the air scatter the light that shines on them. The denser the fog the more the light is scattered, the less of it gets through the fog, and the less one can see through a fog with even the most powerful beam of light. By measuring the fraction of the incident light that goes straight through the fog and the fraction that is scattered by the fog particles, one can estimate the number of water droplets in the fog—or the number of dust particles in the air. This method is accurate for determining the number of fine particles in a cloudy suspension in air or in water and is used frequently in analytical chemistry.

A similar method can be used to determine the number of electrons in the space around the nucleus of atoms. Just think of electrons as small particles forming a suspension around the nucleus. In solid materials, the atoms are rather close to one another, and the electrons form an almost continuous suspension throughout the substance, with an occasional nucleus here and there. Now imagine a beam of light shining through this suspension of electrons. If there are few electrons, only a little light will be scattered by them, and most of it will go right through. But if there are many electrons, much light will be scattered, and only a small fraction of it will get through the material.

Naturally a beam of ordinary light is too coarse for this job. Its wave is so large that it passes over a tiny electron without being in the least affected, much as a huge wave on the ocean washes over a man without being the slightest bit altered in appearance or direction. What we need for the electron suspension is light with a very small wave. Such are X rays, whose wavelength is about ten thousand times smaller than that of ordinary light. When X-ray scattering measurements are made with thin layers of the various elements in the Periodic Table, it turns out that each successive element in order of its atomic number acts as if it has one more electron in the space around the nucleus.

Since hydrogen has one electron, and helium two, lithium must have three, beryllium four, boron five, carbon six, and so on up to uranium, which has ninety-two, and beyond it into the recently discovered series of "artificial" elements. The atomic number, that is the numerical position of an element in the atomic series, gives the number of electrons surrounding the central nucleus of its atom. Notice also that the atomic number places an element in a specific spot in the Periodic Table, and since a specific spot means certain definite chemical properties it follows that the chemical characteristics of an element are determined by the number of electrons surrounding its nucleus. This is an important fact to remember.

The electrons are negative charges. The atom as a whole, however, is neutral. Therefore the nucleus must possess a like number of positive charges to balance the number of electrons around it. One need not accept this on faith, because there are many independent proofs for it. I shall consider one kind of evidence because it follows so simply from the gold-foil experiment described in the preceding section.

The manner in which a stream of alpha particles behaves as it passes through a foil of metal must depend on the charge on the nucleus of the metal. An alpha particle is the positively charged helium nucleus. If it comes near the positively charged nucleus of another atom the alpha particle will be repelled, because like charges repel each other. The extent of repulsion will depend on the charge on the metal nucleus. A large positive charge will repel the alpha particle more than will a small one.

A stream of alpha particles passing through a foil of metal will therefore be scattered to an extent depending on the charge on the metal's nucleus. The higher the atomic number of the metal the more the beam of alpha particles will be scattered, and the precise degree of scattering can be used to determine the charge on the nucleus.

Experiments made on thin foils of many elements bore this reasoning out fully. The scatter in the beam as it passed through various foils behaved as if each successive element in the Periodic Table has one more positive charge on its nucleus than the one preceding it. Again it looks as if the atomic number represents not only the number of electrons but also the number of positive charges on the nucleus of an atom. The two sets of opposite charges balance each other and the result is a neutral atom.

3. THE ATOMIC NUCLEUS PRESENTS DETAILS

We now have an atom composed of a central nucleus surrounded by electrons in a space thousands of times larger than the nucleus. The atomic number, that is the serial number of the element in the Periodic Table, determines the number of electrons as well as the number of balancing positive charges on the nucleus. The atomic weight is essentially the weight of the nucleus, because the electrons weigh so little.

Electrons we know about. They are units of negative electricity and have a mass of only 1/1840 of that of a hydrogen atom. But what is the nucleus, and how are the positive charges and the mass distributed in it? Again it was Rutherford who furnished the answers by experiment and thought.

Rutherford attempted to break up the nuclei of a variety of substances by bombarding them with streams of alpha particles which he could get from radium. He first tried hydrogen gas and watched particularly for those rare times when there was a collision between an alpha particle and something in the hydrogen gas. Even more than in the gold leaf the alpha particle went straight ahead most of the time. But when an alpha particle did hit a hydrogen nucleus it sent it careening. The reason is clear. An alpha particle is four times as heavy as a hydrogen nucleus and is traveling 18,000 miles a second; and when it meets the hydrogen nucleus head on, the impact is a powerful one. However, in spite of this powerful impact, nothing comes out except a positively charged hydrogen nucleus.

Rutherford then tried bombarding nitrogen gas with alpha particles. The frequency of collision was somewhat greater, but spinning out as the result of the collision there again appeared a hydrogen nucleus. He then directed a stream of alpha particles into sodium vapor, and again only the same positively charged hydrogen nucleus appeared as the result of a collision. Nothing smaller or different appeared from other elements similarly exposed to streams of alpha particles. In short, it looked as if the charged hydrogen ion, H^+, is the unit of nuclear structure. This was the first artificially induced transformation of elements. Rutherford's experiment thus marked the beginning of a new era of "atomic chemistry." Since the discovery of natural radioactivity, scientists had known that such transformations do occur spontaneously in nature; now, for the first time, it was found possible to bring them about artificially—although, for the time being, only by using naturally radioactive material as the source of energy.

The charged hydrogen nucleus became so common that it was given a special name. H^+ is called a proton. It has a mass of 1 and a positive charge of 1. Since nothing else was known to come out of nuclei bombarded by alpha particles, it was considered as the unit building block out of which all atomic nuclei are constructed.

This picture of the nucleus raises a pretty question. The atomic number of hydrogen is 1. Therefore its nucleus is a single proton of weight 1 and positive charge 1, and it has 1 electron around it. But consider helium, which has an atomic number of 2. Its atom contains 2 electrons, which are balanced by 2 positive charges on the nucleus. Two positive charges mean 2 protons. But 2 protons weigh only 2 atomic units, and the atomic weight of helium is 4. Where does the additional mass of 2 come from?

The same problem arises for all succeeding elements. Lithium has an atomic number of 3. Hence its nuclear charge is 3, and therefore its nucleus has 3 protons. But its atomic weight is 7, so that 4 units of mass have to be accounted for. Or consider carbon, whose atomic number is 6. Its nucleus has 6 protons. But 6 protons weigh only 6 units, and the atomic weight of carbon is 12. This situation continues to be true, so that the atomic weight of an element beyond hydrogen is about twice as large as its atomic number, and for the heavier elements much more than twice. Thus the atomic number of silver is 47, while its atomic weight is 108; the atomic number of lead is 82, and its atomic weight is 207; the atomic number of uranium is 92, and its atomic weight is 238. What makes up the extra weight of the nucleus?

For about twenty years no one knew the real answer to this puzzle. In the meanwhile one relied on the fact that until then the only particle that had been forced out of the nucleus was the proton. The suggestion was therefore commonly made that the nucleus is really composed of the number of protons corresponding to the atomic *weight*, but that the positive charges in excess of those required by the atomic number are neutralized by a like number of electrons *within* the nucleus.

With the aid of Figure 8 we can work this idea out for a few cases. For example, helium really has 4 protons in the nucleus to give it the mass of 4. But 2 of them are combined with 1 electron each to form 2 neutralized groups, so that the net charge on the nucleus is only 2 positive units. Lithium with an atomic weight of 7 and an atomic number of 3 behaves similarly. It has 7 protons in its nucleus, but of these, 4 are neutralized by 1 electron each *inside* the nucleus leaving a net positive charge of 3, which in turn is balanced by the 3 electrons outside the nucleus.

In this way one can proceed to the higher elements, as for example, uranium, whose atomic number is 92, and whose atomic weight is 238. This statement means that outside the

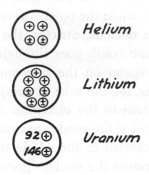

FIGURE 8. SAMPLE ATOMIC NUCLEI

The nuclei of three elements as they were pictured in the years before 1932. Each nucleus contains several protons (+) and several proton-electron combinations (±).

nucleus it has 92 negative electrons, which determine its chemical properties. Its nucleus contains 238 protons, of which 146 are neutralized by an electron each inside the nucleus, leaving a net positive charge of 92 to balance the 92 outside electrons.

This explanation seemed fairly reasonable, but nobody felt comfortable with it. It accounted formally for the facts, but no one was happy with neutralized pairs of protons and electrons inside the nucleus. They left too many questions unanswered.

Such was the situation in 1912, and the problem remained

in this state until 1932. In the interval, other events took place that revealed and clarified other aspects of the structure of the atom.

4. THE ATOM IS A SOLAR SYSTEM

The years that followed the establishment of the nuclear atom saw the development of two lines of experimentation. One was concerned with the arrangements of the electrons around the nucleus, while the other was devoted to exploring the interior of the nucleus. Strictly, the path of our story from atom to atomic bomb goes through the nucleus only, and any time we spend on the surrounding electrons is a diversion. However, for the sake of completeness I propose to devote this section to the electrons. The nucleus is not the whole atom, and if the reader has gone with me so far, he is probably interested in the whole structure. The work on the electrons around the nucleus grew by virtue of ideas developed by Niels Bohr in 1912 almost immediately after Rutherford had originated the concept of the atomic nucleus.

The space in the atom outside the nucleus is enormous compared with the size of the nucleus, or with the much smaller size of an electron. In the atom of hydrogen the single electron is near the outer rim of the atom. If its nucleus were enlarged to the size of a baseball, its electron would be a speck about eight city blocks away. Actually, of course, this atomic distance is small. The diameter of a hydrogen atom is nearly 1/200,000,000 of an inch; in other words, 200,000,000 hydrogen atoms could be placed one next the other in an inch. Relative to the nucleus or to the electron, however, the atomic space is prodigious.

It is in this circumnuclear space that the electrons are

to be found. Obviously, they cannot be there just helter-skelter. When there is so much regularity in the Periodic Table, it is hardly to be expected that the electrons are merely dumped into this outside region without being arranged in some definite system. The whole of chemistry depends on the behavior of some of these electrons because of the way some of them are shared to form the chemical bonds that unite atoms into molecules. Moreover, each element in the Periodic Table has one more electron than its preceding neighbor. Surely the electrons are distributed with some regularity.

Let us look at the Periodic Table (Figure 2) in the vertical column under lithium. It contains the soft alkali metals, lithium, sodium, potassium, rubidium, cesium, and francium, with which we are already acquainted. Hydrogen can be in two columns, and may be included in the present one. All these elements are monovalent: they have one chemical bond. Being monovalent means that they each have one electron on the surface, which can easily be shared with another element.

Hydrogen is monovalent because it has only one electron. But lithium has 3 electrons; yet one of them acts as if it were on the surface, easily available. Similarly, sodium has 11 electrons, and yet one is on the surface for valence purposes. And so on with potassium, which has 19 electrons, one of which is a valence electron; rubidium with a total of 37 electrons, and cesium with 55 electrons, each with one valence electron on the surface of the atom.

It almost looks as if the electrons were arranged in shells, and each time we come around the Periodic Table to the column of alkali metals, a new shell of electrons gets started with the one electron in it. It is this single electron in the new outer shell that is easily available, and that makes these elements similar chemically.

If this idea of shells of electrons is right, then the element that just precedes one of these soft alkali metals should have a complete and stable shell of electrons. Moreover, since the electron shell is complete and stable, there should be no easily detachable electrons, the element should have no valence electrons, and therefore it should be an inert substance, with little tendency to combine with other substances.

Now look at the Periodic Table and see what precedes lithium. Helium does; and helium is an inert gas, one of the noble series. Moreover, neon precedes sodium; argon precedes potassium; krypton precedes rubidium; and xenon precedes cesium. In each case the preceding element is a stable inert gas, which enters into no, or only a very few, chemical combinations. These inert gases are all in the same column. It must be that they have nothing but complete or stable electron shells around the nucleus.

In this way we learn that the first completed electron shell contains 2 electrons and is represented by helium; the second completed shell contains 8 electrons, and corresponds to neon with its total of 10 electrons. Similarly the third shell also has 8 electrons, making a total of 18 electrons in the three shells, and this represents argon. Krypton with its 36 electrons then has four shells of electrons: the first contains 2, the second 8, the third has been enlarged to 18, and the last contains 8 again, as did the outer shells of neon and argon. Then xenon with its 54 electrons has its fourth shell enlarged to have 18 electrons, and its outer fifth shell has 8 electrons as did neon, argon, and krypton. Finally radon, with its 86 electrons, also has 8 electrons in its outer sixth shell. Diagrams of the first five noble gases are shown in Figure 9 for illustration. Eight electrons in the outer shell seems a stable and symmetrical number.

The idea of electron shells is so good that by following it

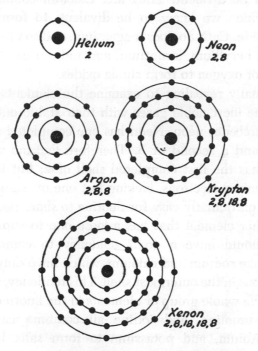

FIG. 9. ELECTRON SHELLS IN THE NOBLE GASES

For helium, two electrons make the first completed shell. Each of the other noble gases has eight electrons in the outer shell, while the inner shells are completely saturated with electrons.

out logically one finds the most illuminating information about atoms and their positions in the Periodic Table. If the elements in the helium column represent completed or stable electron shells, and the elements in the lithium column represent the first electron in a new shell, then the elements in

the beryllium column next to it should contain two electrons in the new shell. These two electrons in the new outer
shell are obviously free to be shared, which means that the
elements in the beryllium column should have two chemical
bonds and be divalent. They are. Calcium combines with
oxygen, which we know to be divalent, to form lime or
calcium oxide, CaO. So does magnesium, and so does barium,
and so do beryllium, strontium, and radium combine with
one atom of oxygen to form stable oxides.

It is equally revealing to examine the elements that just
precede the inert noble gases with their stable outer shells.
Fluorine precedes neon. Neon has one completed shell of 2
electrons and a second of 8. Therefore fluorine with its 9
electrons has the first completed shell of 2; but its second
shell has only 7 electrons, lacking just one of completion. It
should be particularly easy for fluorine to share one electron
with another element that has a loose one to supply. Thus
fluorine should have a great tendency to combine with
elements like sodium and calcium, which have only one and
two electrons in the outermost shell. This tendency, of course,
is true of the whole group of elements in the fluorine column.
Chlorine, bromine, and iodine all combine easily with
sodium, lithium, and potassium to form salts like NaCl
(sodium chloride) and LiCl (lithium chloride), since each
element is monovalent. Also they combine with calcium and
magnesium to form $CaCl_2$ (calcium chloride) and $MgCl_2$
(magnesium chloride), since both calcium and magnesium
are divalent. This kind of reaction tells us that fluorine,
chlorine, and the others in the same column have all their
electron shells completed or stable except for one electron
in the very outermost shell. The same is true of hydrogen,
which has one electron. It may be considered as having one

electron more than nothing, or one less than the complete shell of two that helium has.

If we had the space we could examine many other properties of the elements and find with what astonishing niceness they are predictable from the idea of a series of electron shells surrounding the nucleus. I cannot resist describing just one more property, because it fits in with information that we already have.

Earlier I described how atoms can become electrically charged, and be ions, or wanderers in an electrical field. Since the alkali metals, lithium, sodium, and so on in the same column of the Periodic Table, have each only one electron in a newly formed outer shell, it should be relatively easy to pull this electron off and leave the element electrically unbalanced. Normally the number of positive charges on the nucleus equals the number of negative electrons around the nucleus. If one of these electrons is stripped off, the atom will be left with one extra positive charge and become a positive ion. This is true; the alkali metals do easily form ions like Li^+ (lithium ion), Na^+ (sodium ion), K^+ (potassium ion) and so on, each with one charge.

What is more, the elements in the beryllium column should form divalent ions. Their two electrons should be easily removable; not so easily as the one in the preceding alkali metals, but still fairly easily. This is also true; calcium forms the ion Ca^{++}; magnesium forms the ion Mg^{++}, and so on with the others, each with its two positive charges.

Finally the elements in the boron column should have three electrons in the last shell, and when these are stripped off, the ions should have three positive charges. And so they do: aluminum forms Al^{+++}, cerium forms Ce^{+++}, and so on.

Now consider fluorine, chlorine, and the other elements

in that column. They lack one electron to complete a stable outer electron shell of 8 electrons. This means that one electron can easily slip in, and the atom will have one more electron than the number of positive charges on the nucleus. It will be negatively charged, and will become a negative

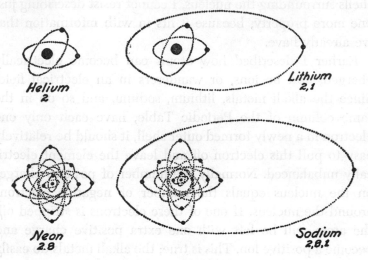

FIGURE 10. ELECTRON ORBITS

A fanciful picture of the paths followed by electrons. Notice helium and neon with their completed shells, and lithium and sodium each with one electron in a new shell.

ion. Thus fluorine becomes F⁻, chlorine Cl⁻, and iodine I⁻, each with a single negative charge.

In Figure 9 the electron shells are shown as circles. Obviously this is because the paper is flat; in reality the shells must be spheres and tridimensional. This is a good first approximation, like assuming that the planets go around the sun in circles. Actually they go in ellipses, and similarly the electron shells are not always spheres. Figure 10 shows a fanciful way in which the electrons may be arranged, especially if one assumes that the electrons move around the nucleus, as indeed one must.

The electron-shell arrangement of the circumnuclear electrons is one of the most beautiful ideas in science. In the simpler atoms the energies of the electrons have been worked out in fair detail, and some of the correspondences that have been first predicted and later discovered are startling in their subtlety. In particular those concerned with the wavelengths of light emitted or absorbed by the elements under various conditions have been studied most rigorously and represent thinking and imagination of the highest order.

One warning is needed here. In 1925 it became evident that any statement concerning the location and motion of an electron at any given instant must be taken with a grain of salt. All such elementary particles are so tiny that any attempt to observe them (for example, by scattering a light beam off them—as dust particles are revealed in a ray of sunlight), changes their position. Hence, all that can be stated accurately about them is the region where they are most likely to be found. Instead of being able to describe precise electron orbits, we must resort to the vaguer picture of "electron clouds" surrounding the nucleus. Thus, in atomic physics precise point mechanics had to bow out and statistical probability calculation took its place!

However, this is not our direction now. Alluring as this field is, we must leave it, and return to the interior of the nucleus to follow the development of its structure as it leads to the fateful realities of the atomic bomb.

IV

ATOMIC STRUCTURE IS COMPLETED

1. ISOTOPES: ATOMS DIFFERENT INSIDE BUT IDENTICAL OUTSIDE

Atoms are made of protons and electrons. A proton weighs 1 unit, and an electron 1/1840 or 0.00054 unit. Since the electron weighs so trifling an amount, why then are the atomic weights of the elements not whole or very nearly whole numbers?

The problem is an old one. Early in the nineteenth century, after Dalton had suggested the atomic theory, Prout had proposed that all atoms were made up of hydrogen. Prout's hypothesis had to be discarded because the atomic weights of the elements were not exact multiples of the weight of hydrogen. This is not a matter of just ordinary accuracy. By 1900, atomic weights had been measured with a precision greater than any other constant of chemistry—to the fourth and fifth decimal places. They were not whole numbers, nor were they exact multiples of the atomic weight of hydrogen. Prout's hypothesis had long been adandoned, and yet here we are adopting essentially the same idea, by assuming that all atoms are made up of protons and electrons. If our theory of atomic structure is correct, why indeed are atomic weights not whole numbers?

Fortunately, this question did not bother investigators for

very long, because by the time Rutherford had established the nuclear structure of the atom, other phenomena had already suggested the answer. The reason that atomic weights are not whole numbers is that the elements as usually isolated and purified chemically are not single atomic species but mixtures. This statement needs to be explained and justified.

Take the element ionium. In 1906 this was a new element, which had just been discovered by B. B. Boltwood at Yale. He had isolated it from pitchblende, the mineral that contains a lot of uranium, and from which the Curies several years before had extracted radium and startled the world. Further study showed that the chemical properties of ionium were very much like those of thorium. It had the same appearance, the same solubilities, the same melting point, and even the same color characteristics as thorium. Yet the two differed in atomic weight. The atomic weight of ionium is 231.5; that of thorium is 232.1.

Direct comparison of ionium and thorium made certain that chemically the two were not merely similar; they were identical. If the two were mixed it became impossible to separate them. Separation is largely a chemical procedure depending on differences between substances in solubility, boiling point, or combining capacity. When two different substances are dissolved in one solution, the addition of another liquid may well precipitate one substance while the other remains in solution. But thorium and ionium have identical chemical properties and cannot be separated. Yet they cannot be the same because their atomic weights are different.

True, the difference in atomic weight is only 0.6, and seems small. However, the very fact that atomic weights can be determined with great precision to several decimal places makes a difference of 0.6 as certain and real as anything can be. Here, therefore, are two substances with the same chemical properties but different atomic weights.

This is indeed a riddle. But in this case the riddles came in pairs. It will be recalled that radium spontaneously gives off alpha particles, electrons, and gamma rays, and leaves radium emanation or radon. Radon is itself radioactive, and in a little while breaks down to radium-A, which is also radioactive and leaves radium-B, which breaks down to radium-C, and so on through several transformations ending in a substance that is stable and that looks like lead. It has not only the same appearance, but the same chemical properties, the same color characteristics, and all the common attributes of lead. If it is mixed with ordinary lead, the two cannot be separated from the mixture. Yet the two have different origins.

What adds to the puzzle is that there exists still another form of lead. The element thorium, whose atomic number is 90, is spontaneously radioactive and forms a family of radioactive sequences much as radium does. The end of this sequence is a stable substance that also looks and behaves like ordinary lead.

It was Frederick Soddy who as early as 1910 saw the meaning of these riddles of ionium-thorium and of the three different leads that are alike. With fine courage he predicted that the three leads would have different atomic weights, and that the one from thorium would be greater than ordinary lead while the one from radium would be less than ordinary lead. Independently Kasimir Fajans made a similar prediction. Both turned out to be correct. The atomic weight of ordinary lead is 207.2. The atomic weight of thorium lead is 207.9, while the atomic weight of radium lead is 206.1.

The one is 0.7 greater and the other 1.1 less than ordinary lead. These values were secured by the great masters of atomic weight determinations, Theodore W. Richards in America, and O. Hönigschmid in Germany, and there was no wishing them away. Here are elements identical chemically but with different atomic weights. How can this be?

Soddy called such substances isotopes, and explained what they represent in terms of atomic structure. In Greek *iso* means alike or the same; and *topos* means spot or space. Isotopes are atomic species that occupy the same space in the Periodic Table, having the same atomic number and the same chemical properties, regardless of what their atomic weights may be.

We have learned that the chemical properties of an element are determined by the number of its electrons outside the nucleus, which of course equals the net number of positive charges on the nucleus. Therefore, if two atoms are indistinguishable chemically, they must be varieties of a single element, with the same number of positive charges on the nucleus and the same number of electrons outside the nucleus, arranged identically in their shells.

However, we have also learned that the nucleus contains more than the protons necessary to give it its net charge. For instance, helium has 2 protons in the nucleus, which gives it its 2 positive charges; but because its atomic weight is 4, it has something else in the nucleus that supplies the extra mass of 2.

At this time it had been tentatively supposed that this extra nuclear mass of 2 is furnished by 2 additional protons, each of which is neutralized by 1 electron inside the nucleus. In the same way lithium, with its atomic weight of 7 and atomic number of 3, has 7 protons in the nucleus, of which 4 are neutralized by 4 electrons inside the nucleus, leaving a net nuclear charge of 3.

Now suppose that a lithium atom is composed somewhat differently, as shown in Figure 11. Suppose that it has only 6 protons in the nucleus, and that 3 of these are internally neutralized by 3 electrons. The nucleus still has 3 positive charges, and the atom has 3 outside electrons arranged in

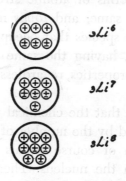

FIGURE 11. ISOTOPES OF LITHIUM

All three isotopes have the same number of protons, and therefore the same net 3 positive charges on the nucleus. Three positive charges also mean 3 electrons. Hence the three isotopes are chemically alike. However, the extra mass of "neutralized protons" makes the difference between the masses of the isotopes, each being 1 unit heavier than its lighter neighbor.

two shells as before. Since the chemical properties are determined by the electrons in their shells, this atom would be indistinguishable chemically from the regular lithium atom. It would have the same atomic number, 3, and occupy the same spot in the Periodic Table. Its atomic weight, however, would be less by 1 unit than normal lithium; its atomic weight would be 6 instead of 7.

Or suppose that an atom has 8 protons in the nucleus, of which 5 are internally neutralized by 5 electrons. The net charge on the nucleus would again be 3, and the atom would again have 3 outside electrons arranged in two shells. Such an atom would have all the chemical properties of lithium; its atomic number would be 3 and it would be in the same spot as lithium in the Periodic Table. But its atomic weight would be 8 instead of 7.

According to Soddy these three types of lithium would be isotopes: three chemically identical substances with different atomic weights. In this way Soddy explained ionium and thorium, and the three kinds of lead. Ionium and thorium are isotopes; they have the same atomic number (90), the same number of nuclear charges, the same number of electrons outside the nucleus arranged in the same shells. But they differ in the number of internally neutralized protons present in the nucleus to make up the different atomic weights. Similarly, lead, radium-lead, and thorium-lead are isotopes: they have the same atomic number (82), with the usual chemical consequences, but they differ in the number of internally neutralized protons in the nucleus that determine their atomic weights.

This idea of Soddy's explains why ionium and thorium, though identical chemically, differ in atomic weight. But how does it explain the fact that neither atomic weight is a whole number? Soddy knew the answer to this. Neither ionium nor thorium is a pure isotope; each is a mixture.

It is simpler to examine lithium. We saw a moment ago that it is conceivable to have three kinds of lithium, which are chemically indistinguishable isotopes: the normal one whose atomic weight is 7, a light one of atomic weight 6, and a heavy one of atomic weight 8. Suppose that ordinary lithium as found in nature is a mixture of two of these three isotopes, the normal one and the light one. If they were mixed in equal proportions the atomic weight of the mixture would be midway between 6 and 7 or 6.5. Actually the atomic weight of lithium is 6.94, which is so near 7 that the light isotope probably occurs about once in twenty atoms of the mixture.

Let us suppose that most elements as they are found in nature are mixtures of isotopes. It then follows that the deviations of atomic weights from whole numbers can serve as a clue to the relative amounts of the different isotopes in the elements as they occur naturally. This has turned out to be true. However, in 1910 it was guesswork, brilliant and sublime guesswork of the kind that gives one's heart a lift even in retrospect. GIVE ME A BREAK!

Before closing this section we may as well learn how to designate isotopes, because we need them later in the story. Again let us use lithium as an easy example. Lithium has an atomic number of 3. Its common isotope has an atomic weight of 7. This isotope is therefore written as $_3Li^7$; the subscript 3 indicates the atomic number, while the superscript 7 gives the atomic weight. Its less common isotope is $_3Li^6$. The theoretical isotope $_3Li^8$, which I described a while back, has never been found; it is inherently unstable. Frequently the isotopes are just referred to by their weights, and the atomic number is omitted because it is well known. Thus we speak of lithium-6 or lithium-7; and of the nonexistent isotope as lithium-8.

Now we can return to the story itself. Soon after this time many isotopes were discovered, but in a way quite different from what one would expect from the development that drove Soddy to invent them.

2. ISOTOPES IN BUNCHES

Let us go back to our old Geissler tubes and see what happened with them. A Geissler tube is a glass tube from which most of the air has been pumped out and through which an electric current passes between two metal electrodes. One of these plates is negative and from it a steady stream of electrons goes across the space to the other plate, which is positive. The negative plate is the cathode; the positive one is the anode.

As the current passes through the gas in the tube it tends to strip the negative electrons from the atoms of the gas and carry them along, from the cathode to the anode. What remains of the atoms are positively charged ions, which must be moving in the opposite direction, from the anode toward the negative cathode. These streams of positive ions were called positive rays when they were first discovered, and it was their study that developed our knowledge of isotopes.

In order to investigate these positive rays, J. J. Thomson designed a tube somewhat different from those previously used. If positive rays are coming from right to left, as they are shown in Figure 12, it would be a good idea to catch them and find out what they are. Therefore, Thomson used a thick cathode, and drilled a long hole in its center, in the hope that the positive rays on their way toward the cathode would go right through the hole and pass beyond it in a straight beam. For this reason he lengthened the tube to the left of the cathode and made arrangements to put a photographic plate at the extreme end. He argued that the beam of positive rays would impinge on the photographic plate and make a little black spot the diameter of the beam. And that is precisely what happened.

The next step was even more exciting than the mere demonstration of the existence of positive rays. If these rays are really the atoms of the gas stripped of some electrons, that is, if they are ions, then they should have essentially the mass of the atoms of the gas in the nearly evacuated

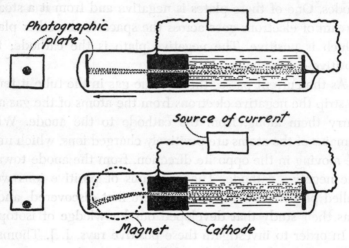

FIGURE 12. DEMONSTRATION OF POSITIVE RAYS

The upper drawing shows the positive rays going through the hole in the cathode and falling on a photographic plate to make a round spot in the center. The lower drawing shows a magnet deflecting the beam so that it hits the photographic plate at a spot lower down on the photograph.

tube. Thomson knew how to measure such masses, for it was he who had measured the mass of the electron several years before. He used the same principle here. A powerful magnet placed near the tube should divert the positively charged particles from their direct path. Instead of hitting the photographic plate dead center, the beam should hit below or above depending upon the orientation of the magnet. Moreover, the beam of charged particles should be deflected more or less, depending upon the mass of particles. Heavy particles should be deflected less than light particles, and if there are several kinds of ion in the beam of positive rays, there should be several spots on the photographic plate at distances from the center depending on the masses of the ions.

The first gas that Thomson used in this apparatus was neon. Nowadays the red color of neon under such conditions is familiar in the common neon signs. In 1910 it was relatively rare. The gas that J. J. Thomson used was highly purified neon, and when its positive rays were deflected by a magnet and photographed at the other end of the tube, it showed a dense dark spot at a distance from the center corresponding to a mass of 20. Neon has an atomic weight of just over 20 and this fits the requirements.

In addition to this dark spot corresponding to neon, there was a very much lighter spot farther from the center at a place corresponding to something with an atomic weight of 4. This lighter spot was clearly helium. We already know that helium and neon are both inert gases belonging in the same vertical column in the Periodic Table, and it is easy to understand why one could not remove all the slightest impurities of elements similar to neon. In fact, there was still another spot evident on the photographic plate; this one at a place corresponding to an atomic weight of 40. This also seemed sensible, because argon has an atomic weight of 39.9, and argon is another of the inert noble gases in the same column of the Periodic Table.

So far, so good. However, close examination of the photograph showed a very fine shadow of a spot at a place near neon but corresponding to an atomic weight of 22. J. J. Thomson purified his neon several times; but whenever any tube showed a spot for neon at 20, it always showed a faint shadow at 22. Could it be that there are two kinds of neon, which cannot be separated from each other by chemical purification, a neon of atomic weight 20, and a neon of atomic weight 22? If there were two kinds of neon, then the reason that even the most purified neon gas has an atomic weight of 20.18 is that it is a mixture of the two neon isotopes, with neon-22 present as a small fraction of the mixture.

These observations were made about 1913 in the Cavendish Laboratory, Cambridge University, where J. J. Thomson was the director. F. W. Aston, one of the younger men there, thought he saw a way of making certain that these ideas were correct. Aston argued that even if one cannot separate the two neons by chemical means, one should be able to separate them by physical means, using some property that depends on the mass of the nucleus, rather than on the number of electrons. For example, suppose we liquefy neon, and then let it evaporate slowly. The atoms of neon-22 are 10 per cent heavier than the atoms of neon-20. The atoms of the heavier isotopes should therefore find it a little more difficult to hurl themselves from liquid neon into the air and become gaseous neon. The lighter neon will thus evaporate faster than the heavier neon, and after most of the liquid neon has evaporated, the residue should contain a larger fraction of heavy neon than before.

Aston tried out his idea in this way, but failed to find any differences. He therefore tested another method involving the same idea. He allowed neon to diffuse from one container into another through a barrier of baked clay like that used for clay pipes. This clay is a porous material full of microscopic holes, through which the neon atoms would have to travel. Aston argued that the heavy neon isotope should not be able to move so rapidly as the light neon, and therefore that the gas that had passed through the clay barrier would contain less of the heavier isotope, whereas the gas remaining in the original container would have more of the heavier isotope. Aston found a just measurable difference between the gases in the two containers, enough to show the probability of the idea, but not enough to settle the matter.

These two methods are mentioned here because they are typical of the kind that were later used successfully. Indeed, much later they were important in the manufacture of materials for the atomic bomb. Unfortunately their first trials by Aston resulted in little more than encouragement.

This was in 1914, just when the First World War began. Most of the young men in England became occupied with the war, and nothing much happened in the laboratories. Aston survived the war and in 1919, when he again began working in this field, he did not return to the separation experiments, but followed more directly in J. J. Thomson's footsteps.

Aston elaborated the negative end of the Geissler tube to an even greater extent than had J. J. Thomson. In addition to the one hole in the cathode through which positive ions passed, he placed another block of metal with another hole farther to the left, as in Figure 13. In this way the stream of positive ions that goes through the first hole, and that has become slightly divergent by the time it reaches the second hole, is sharpened because the second hole permits the passage of only those ions that have gone in a straight line between the first and second holes. By this means a very precise beam of ions is formed, which makes a small spot when it hits the photographic plate at the end of the tube. When a large magnet is put outside near this beam of ions, the beam curves away from its original direction in an arc whose curvature is determined by the mass of the ion. In this way one gets a series of spots on the photographic plate, and the spacing of the spots depends on the masses of the ions which make up the beam. Since the mass of an ion is

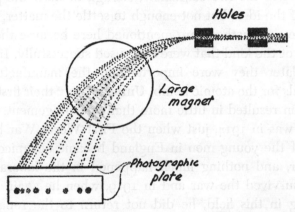

FIGURE 13. MASS SPECTROMETER FOR ISOTOPE SEPARATION

This is the left or cathode end of a Geissler tube, enlarged and modified. The large magnet curves the particles of different mass to different extents, the lighter being deflected more than the heavier.

essentially the mass of its nucleus, this procedure is a method of separating isotopes.

Before the First World War Thomson had found the secondary light spot of neon-22 associated with the darker spot of neon-20, and had recognized them as the two isotopes of neon. With his new and precise instrument Aston found that practically all elements, even when thoroughly purified, have these secondary spots associated with them. It was comparatively easy to determine the relative weights of the ions corresponding to the various spots, and in a short time Aston found the isotopes of many elements. Moreover, since the degree of blackening of a spot depends on the number of ions that hit it, Aston could also gauge the relative abundance of the isotopes of any element. The sketch at the bottom of Figure 13 shows how such a photographic plate looks.

Aston found that almost all the elements he studied have isotopes. His work was later taken up by K. T. Bainbridge in the United States, and between them they examined the whole series of elements, which were found to have from one to eight isotopes. All the first ninety-two elements together have a total of approximately two hundred and fifty isotopes. A strange regularity has turned up here. Those elements whose atomic number is even usually have a greater number of isotopes than those elements whose atomic number is odd.

Our original question of why the atomic weights of the elements are not whole numbers can now be answered with confidence. Most elements are mixtures of isotopes. The fractions in their atomic weights depend on the relative proportions in which the isotopes exist in nature. If an element has an atomic weight that is very nearly an integer, it is overwhelmingly composed of just one isotope. This is true of fluorine, with its atomic weight of 19.00; of sodium, with its weight of 23.00; and of helium, with its weight of 4.00.

3. A SPECIAL ISOTOPE: HEAVY HYDROGEN

The existence of numerous isotopes presents us with a pretty problem. Very early the atomic weight of oxygen had been assigned the arbitrary value of 16.000. This was fine before anyone knew about isotopes and would still be fine if oxygen had no isotopes and were just $_8O^{16}$. But oxygen has two naturally occurring isotopes, O^{17} and O^{18}. For every five hundred atoms of O^{16} there is an atom either of O^{17} or of O^{18}. If we assign the value of 16.000 to the isotope O^{16}, then the atomic weight as determined with the naturally occurring mixture of oxygen isotopes will have to be higher by nearly 3 parts in 16,000; that is, it will be 16.003.

For most purposes this difference need not even be remembered, because it is so trifling. It does make a difference in the atomic weights of the other elements, which would all have to be raised by the same fraction. Therefore to avoid confusion, the old value of 16.000 for natural oxygen has been retained as the standard. But the difference, slight as it is, did set people thinking about hydrogen.

Without going into the details of the argument one can report that if the hydrogen atom is really just one proton and one electron, then the atomic weight of ordinary hydrogen is too high by the same amount, that is, by 3 parts in 16,000, or about 1 part in 5000. Please remember that even twenty years ago the atomic weight of hydrogen had been measured repeatedly with the greatest precision, and was known as precisely 1.00778. An error of 0.02 per cent was out of the question. Therefore this difference had to be accounted for.

It could be explained most easily if hydrogen had a heavy isotope. But unfortunately neither Aston nor Bainbridge had been able to find any trace of an isotope of hydrogen. Hydrogen purified and put through the glorified Geissler tube (now called a mass spectrometer) showed only one spot in the proper place, and no more.

There was always the bare possibility that a heavy isotope of hydrogen does exist, but is present in so small a concentration as not to affect the photographic plate of Aston's and Bainbridge's mass spectrometer. Computation had shown that if a heavy isotope of hydrogen exists, then its presence as only 1 part in 5000 parts of normal hydrogen would account for the discrepancy in atomic weight. But how can one demonstrate a suspected isotope in such great dilution that no trace of it can be found by the latest and most refined physical method of measurement?

The possibility, however, was fascinating, and for an excellent reason. The usual hydrogen atom has 1 proton, 1 electron, and an atomic weight of 1. The suspected isotope must have 2 protons in its nucleus, one of which is presumably neutralized internally by an electron. This leaves a net charge of 1 on the nucleus, as before, which is balanced by 1 electron outside the nucleus. The weight of this atom is 2, which is twice as much as that of the normal hydrogen atom. This is a real difference in weight.

The difference between neon-20 and neon-22 is only 10 per cent, and Aston's efforts to separate them by diffusion and by evaporation had been largely unsuccessful. Moreover, the efforts to separate chlorine isotopes had also succeeded only very slightly because of the small difference in weight between the two isotopes Cl^{35} and Cl^{37}. However, with hydrogen there was the possibility of an isotope with twice the weight of common hydrogen. If the ideas behind Aston's effort at separating the neon isotopes by diffusion or evaporation are sound, they should work with hydrogen, if they worked at all.

So Harold C. Urey thought, and as a consequence he decided to make the attempt. Urey argued that if liquid hydrogen were allowed to evaporate slowly, the normal light isotope should go off into the air more easily than the suspected isotope which is twice as heavy. Therefore, as the hydrogen evaporates, the liquid residue should become richer in the heavy isotope, until it becomes sufficiently concentrated to show up on the photographic plate of a mass spectrometer.

Urey interested F. G. Brickwedde at the Bureau of Standards, who proceeded to make a gallon of liquid hydrogen. Brickwedde then allowed the liquid to evaporate slowly until only a gram (1/28 of an ounce) of liquid hydrogen was left, which he shipped to Urey. At Columbia University, Urey and G. M. Murphy introduced a little of this presumably enriched hydrogen into a mass spectrometer, and photographed the positive rays produced, as worked out by Aston. They got the usual spot of hydrogen on the plate, but in addition they found another spot, never seen before, at the place corresponding to an atomic weight of 2. This spot could mean nothing else but the heavy isotope of hydrogen, $_1H^2$.

For this exciting discovery Urey was awarded a Nobel Prize in 1934. For some reason this heavy isotope of hydrogen, $_1H^2$, seemed such a unique particle at the time that it was given a special name, "deuterium," and a separate symbol, D. And just as the nucleus of ordinary hydrogen is called a "proton," the nucleus of deuterium was called a "deuteron."

Water is composed of two atoms of hydrogen and one of oxygen. Obviously deuterium can replace hydrogen in all chemical reactions because the two are isotopes. Therefore, it is to be expected that the compounds DHO and D_2O exist, with one or two heavy hydrogens in place of ordinary hydrogen. Such molecules are called "heavy water." A small fraction of ordinary water must be heavy water. It now became a problem of separating these heavy-water molecules from ordinary water molecules, or at least of increasing their concentration. Such enriched water was prepared by evaporation of ordinary water according to the same principles that led to the discovery of deuterium in the first place.

The concentration of heavy water in the enriched mixture can be measured by weight. The ordinary water molecule weighs 18, its 1 oxygen atom contributing 16 and its 2 hydrogen atoms 1 each. The heavy water molecule weighs 19 or 20 because deuterium atoms contribute 2 each. In the case of D_2O this means a difference of 2 parts in 20, or 1 in 10. In the laboratory one can easily weigh with a precision of 1 part in 10,000. Therefore one can detect by weight 1 part of D_2O in 1000 parts of ordinary water.

The ease and precision of detecting heavy water made it a useful tool in fields other than atomic structure; for example, in physiology. Ordinary water and heavy water are indistinguishable chemically, and even the human body uses them indiscriminately. If you drink some ordinary water today it is not possible to tell how long it stays in the body or where. But if you drink some heavy water, it is possible by its weight to tell the moment it reaches the urine: the water prepared from the urine will be denser than ordinary water.

Heavy hydrogen can be substituted for ordinary hydrogen in a variety of compounds, and their course through the body may be traced in the same way. Indeed, several investigators have studied the path not only of heavy hydrogen but of heavy oxygen O^{18} and of other isotopes as well, so that an entirely new chapter in physiology is now being written.

Deuterium has served as a tool in the further exploration of atomic structure, and heavy water later played a role in the release of atomic energy. The discovery of deuterium and heavy water in itself helped to confirm the explanation of isotopes and to strengthen the meaning of atomic weights.

4. THE BASIS FOR ISOTOPES: NEUTRONS

The discovery of isotopes and the explanation of their structure brought into focus a problem that we have lightly passed over. It concerns the mass of the nucleus in excess of the protons furnishing its net positive charge.

It will be recalled, for example, that lithium with an atomic number of 3 and an atomic weight of 7 has 3 protons in the nucleus and 3 electrons outside. Four units of mass left in the nucleus must be accounted for. For a number of years, this extra mass was tentatively regarded as due to 4 protons whose charges have been neutralized by electrons inside the nucleus; and the diagrams in Figure 8 and Figure 11 were drawn according to this idea.

All the elements above hydrogen have this extra mass in the nucleus; for the heavier atoms it is greater than the mass of the protons responsible for the atomic number and the net charge. Thus uranium has 92 protons with their positive charges, and 146 other units of mass, which were tentatively supposed to be protons whose charges have been neutralized by an electron each within the nucleus.

There were lively arguments as to how an electron can be inside the nucleus and why the positive and negative charges did not annihilate each other. The whole idea seemed strange and no one was satisfied with it. However, the only way to deal with strange things is to ask questions, make experiments, and think about them. Many physicists therefore devoted their attention to the nucleus and tried to explore its structure further by bombarding it with alpha particles from radium, and with protons.

In 1930 W. Bothe and H. Becker sent streams of alpha particles at beryllium, the light metal that is number 4 in the series of elements. What came from the beryllium was a beam of rays with very high penetrating power. Bothe and Becker thought that these rays might be gamma rays like those given off by radium. In this they were later shown to be mistaken.

Frédéric Joliot and his wife Irène Curie, the daughter of Pierre and Marie Curie, made similar experiments in 1932 with beryllium and found that some of the radiation given off by beryllium was able to penetrate a lead shield that normally absorbs gamma rays. In addition, they observed that if a paraffin-shield or any other hydrogen-containing compound were placed around the beryllium, the rays that entered the paraffin caused the ejection of protons of very high energy. This phenomenon was difficult to understand, and prompted others to investigate it.

Within the year, James Chadwick repeated these experiments with beryllium, and found, of course, the same powerful rays as had Bothe and Becker and the Joliot-Curies. He determined that the rays could not be deflected by a magnet —a finding that showed them to be neutral and in this respect like gamma rays or X rays. Chadwick, however, noticed that these rays traveled only at about one-tenth the velocity of light, a speed too slow for gamma rays. Gamma rays travel with the speed of light, since they are a form of light.

Furthermore, Chadwick found that these rays from beryllium, when directed against nitrogen, would give an occasional nitrogen atom a terrific wallop, something that gamma rays could not do, since they will bounce off even such tiny particles as electrons. This impact with the nitrogen atom indicated that the rays must be made of particles, and if they are particles, then they must be neutral particles, because they are not deflected by a magnet.

It was not long before Chadwick was able to show that this neutral particle has a mass of 1, the same as a proton. Very properly he called it a "neutron." For its discovery Chadwick was awarded a Nobel Prize in 1935.

The discovery of the neutron resulted in a huge surge of activity in nuclear physics, and is one of the definitive steps on the road to the atomic bomb. For our immediate purposes, however, its discovery resolved the problem of the extra mass in the nucleus. The extra mass is composed of neutrons. The particles inside the nucleus that give it the necessary weight in addition to its protons are the neutrons. The helium nucleus now contains 2 protons and 2 neutrons, and no hypothetical intranuclear electrons are needed. The lithium nucleus contains 3 protons and 4 neutrons, and so on for the other elements.

We may now rest easy. The charge on the nucleus is entirely due to the protons in it. Its mass, and therefore its atomic weight, is determined by the combined mass of its protons and its neutrons. And since the atomic weight of all elements except hydrogen is at least twice its atomic number, there are at least as many neutrons in a nucleus as there are protons.

The nuclei of some of the elements are shown in Figure 14. Notice particularly aluminum with its 13 protons and 14 neutrons; and barium with its 56 protons and 81 neutrons. And above all, look at uranium with its 92 protons and 146

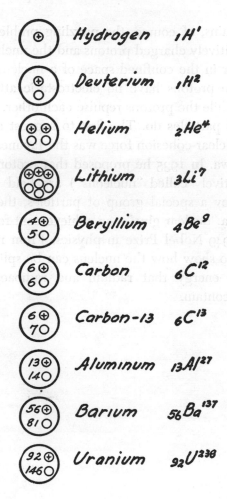

FIGURE 14. NUCLEI OF ATOMS

The number of protons and neutrons in the nuclei are shown for some interesting atoms. For convenience, all nuclei are drawn the same size; actually they differ in size depending on the number of particles in them.

neutrons. All these elements and their isotopes will interest us later.

There remains, of course, the puzzling problem of what holds the positively charged protons and the uncharged neutrons together in the confined space of a nucleus. The neutrons and the protons have no electrostatic attraction for each other, while the protons repulse each other, as all similarly charged particles do. The first to suggest an explanation of the nuclear-cohesion force was the Japanese physicist Hideki Yukawa. In 1935 he proposed that protons and neutrons (collectively called "nucleons") are held together in the nucleus by a special group of particles, the "mesons," which act as a "nuclear glue"—an achievement for which he received a 1949 Nobel Prize in physics. From now on our task will be to show how the nucleus can be split to release the fabulous energy that radium and radioactivity have shown it to contain.

V

ATOMS RELEASE ENERGY

1. MATTER AND ENERGY

By 1935 three fundamental particles of which all matter seemed to be constructed were known: the electron, the proton, and the neutron. We also knew how these particles are distributed inside and outside the nucleus to form that significant sequence of elements represented by the Periodic Table. The picture appeared complete, and its pattern seemed logically sensible and esthetically satisfying.

True. But it left some old questions unanswered, and raised some new ones. Take the matter of radium. Its atomic number is 88 and its atomic weight 226. We can therefore construct its atom by taking 88 protons and 138 neutrons in a tight bunch and surrounding them with 88 electrons arranged in their proper shells. This structure is designed to satisfy the requirements of the Periodic Table and of a host of chemical and physical properties. But why is this structure so unstable that a small grain of radium, all by itself, pours out a powerful stream of alpha particles, beta particles, gamma rays, and heat? Where do the particles and rays come from? Where does the energy come from?

Take the even simpler problem of the neutron. The proton and the neutron both have a mass of 1. Are they related? Could the neutron be a proton that has captured an electron internally, and has become permanently neutralized? Or is the basic particle the neutron, and a proton merely a neutron that has captured a unit of positive electricity?

This last question requires a moment of explanation, because it has introduced a new concept, a unit of positive electricity. Before 1932 the unit charge of positive electricity had always been associated with the particle of mass 1, the proton. However, there were some possibilities that a positive charge might exist separately from this large mass and that there is a unit of positive electricity with a mass of the same order as the electron but opposite in charge. In fact, P. A. M. Dirac predicted in 1931 that such a positive particle must exist, and in 1932 it was actually found by C. D. Anderson. It is called a "positron." It has a mass as small as that of the electron and it is positively charged. It is not very common, and it lives only a short time, because it is neutralized almost as soon as it is formed.

Since 1945, it has become clear that the proton, neutron, and electron are only the most common and most accessible members of a much larger family of "elementary" particles. Of these particles, only the proton, the electron, and an extremely elusive particle called the neutrino, which has no mass and no electric charge, as well as their anti-particles (such as the negatively charged proton and the positively charged electron—the positron), are infinitely stable, barring collisions with other particles. The neutron is *not* stable; its average lifetime is 10^{13} seconds, and it disintegrates spontaneously into a proton, an electron, and a neutrino. Other elementary particles have lifetimes of less than a microsecond and make only a fleeting appearance in such devices as cloud chambers, bubble chambers, or photographic emulsions, designed to detect their paths.

One exciting fact about the more than thirty elementary particles is that each—or almost each—particle has its anti-particle. For charged particles the anti-particle has the opposite charge (for example, the electron and the positron), but for neutral particles the distinction is more subtle. The so-called field particles, postulated to explain electromagnetic forces (photons), gravitational forces (gravitrons), and nuclear attraction forces (Yukawa particles, known also as pi-mesons), are exceptions, having no anti-particles.

But this new fascinating field of particle physics is outside the scope of this book. For our purposes we must restrict ourselves to atomic nuclei consisting of protons and neutrons, held together by pi-mesons.

Since nuclei are made of protons and neutrons, it was expected that the atomic weight of each pure isotope would be a whole-number multiple of the atomic weight of hydrogen. This is true of a few of the lighter elements, such as helium, carbon, and nitrogen, to the second decimal place. But as the masses of the isotopes began to be determined more accurately, it was found not to be true for most of them and not even for the lighter elements when determined to the third and fourth decimal places. For example, the mass of helium $_2He^4$ turned out to be 4.0028, and of carbon $_6C^{12}$, 12.0036.

Remember that this is all on the basis of oxygen as 16.0000. Therefore it might seem that if oxygen were given a slightly different value, everything would come out right. Unfortunately this cannot help, because some of the isotopes actually weigh less than they should, and no amount of arithmetical juggling can make them come out whole numbers. Close study of these circumstances brings out something of first-rate importance.

As usual, let us first work it out for a light element like helium. Many accurate measurements have established that, compared with oxygen as 16.00000, the mass of the proton is 1.00758, and the mass of the neutron is 1.00893. Helium is $_2He^4$ and has 2 protons and 2 neutrons.

$$2 \text{ protons} = 2.01516$$
$$2 \text{ neutrons} = 2.01786$$
$$\text{sum} = 4.03302$$
$$_2He^4 = 4.00280$$
$$\text{Difference} = 0.03022$$

As the table shows, the whole of helium $_2He^4$ is less than the sum of its parts. There is no wishing this difference away; it results from the most accurate measurements imaginable. In the formation of helium from its components 0.03022 unit of mass remains to be accounted for.

One cannot say that the mass is lost. Nothing can be lost. Every physical and chemical transaction balances both in mass and energy. What then has happened? The interesting thing is that Einstein had thought about this back in 1905 in connection with the special theory of relativity. At that time, he had suggested that energy and mass are different aspects of the same basic cosmic stuff, and that the two can be converted one into the other. He wrote a simple equation for the relation between the two, which says merely that energy E is equal to mass m.

Energy is measured in units such as ergs or calories or kilowatt-hours, whereas mass is measured in different units such as grams or pounds. To make mass and energy equal, the unit of mass must be translated into the unit of energy. The same holds even when one unit of mass is translated into another. To translate kilograms into pounds we multiply by a constant number 2.2. So 1 kilogram equals 2.2 pounds. To translate inches into centimeters we multiply by a constant whose value is 2.5. Thus 1 inch equals 2.5 centimeters. Einstein showed that the translating constant for converting mass measured in grams into energy measured in ergs is equal to the square of the velocity of light measured in centimeters per second. The velocity of light is usually designated by the letter c, and its value is 30,000,000,000 centimeters per second. (This is 186,000 miles per second.) The translation constant is c^2, and Einstein's equation becomes $E = mc^2$, probably the most important equation in history.

In 1905 Einstein wondered how to test this equation experimentally, and suggested that it might apply to the enormous energies released in radioactivity, which had only recently been discovered. Einstein's equation was actually tested with alpha particles from the disintegration of lithium-7 by protons by J. D. Cockcroft and E. T. S. Walton. But little did Einstein imagine then that his equation would be demonstrated forty years later on so large a scale as it was at Hiroshima, Nagasaki, and Bikini.

If you compute the energy that the transformation of 0.030 unit of mass yields in terms of the equation, the result is startling. The loss of 0.030 unit of mass in the formation of helium from 2 protons and 2 neutrons represents a disappearance of 3 parts of mass in 400 parts, or about 3/4 of 1 per cent. In one gram (1/28 of an ounce) this is a loss of 0.0075 gram. Multiply this by c^2 and you get over 650 million billion ergs of energy. Translated into common units, this is about 200,000 kilowatt-hours, which is the current used to run 200,000 lamps of 100 watts each for a 10-hour day. And all this from the slight loss in mass that occurs when 1/2 gram each of protons and neutrons unite to form 1 gram of helium.

2. MASS IS CONVERTED TO ENERGY

What happens when 3/4 of 1 per cent of matter is transformed into energy and is liberated in the formation of helium from protons and neutrons? The same thing that happens when a rock rolls down the mountainside and settles in the valley: the final situation is more stable than the initial one. The rock high on the mountain is in a relatively unstable position; if it is dislodged, it will roll downhill. When it comes tearing down the slope, it gives out the energy that it had by virtue of its high location. When the rock ends in the valley, it has less energy available than before, and is more stable; it can no longer roll down that hill.

Stated formally, this means that when a system emits energy during a change it is more stable after the emission than before. A ball, when it falls from the top of a house, gives off energy in its fall, and is in a much more stable position on the ground than on the roof. Water in the ocean has poured down from the hilltops and has given off energy that can be used to make electricity. The water in the ocean is certainly in a more stable condition than it would be on top of a hill.

What is true for these physical changes is also true for chemical changes. When a chemical reaction is accompanied by the emission of energy, the final compounds are more stable than the initial compounds. For example, the bond between carbon and hydrogen has much more energy than the bond between carbon and oxygen. Gasoline, wood, and

TNT have many carbon-hydrogen bonds, and therefore are relatively unstable: they can catch fire or explode. When they do so, they form carbon-oxygen bonds that contain less energy; the energy is given off and the final compounds like carbon dioxide are very stable. In combustion with free oxygen, the replacement of loose oxygen-oxygen bonds by stable oxygen-hydrogen bonds in water adds substantially to the liberated energy.

Precisely the same circumstances attend the emission of energy in the formation of a helium nucleus from protons and neutrons: the helium nucleus is more stable than the neutron or the proton. Neutrons quickly become attached to other elements, whereas helium nuclei, which are the same as alpha particles, stand a good deal of knocking around without becoming attached to anything or without being broken into their components.

One way to judge the relative stability of a system is to determine the energy necessary to change it into some other state. Our rock in the valley is more stable than on the mountaintop because a lot of energy is required to drag it up the mountainside to its original position. It takes a lot of energy to break up a helium nucleus into its protons and neutrons. And since it is difficult to concentrate such an amount of energy in order to supply it to the small nucleus, the result is that an alpha particle, or a helium atom, is a very stable particle indeed. However, it is by no means the most stable nucleus. In fact, it is one of the relatively less stable elements, as we shall see.

The loss of mass that occurs in the formation of a nucleus from protons and neutrons is spoken of as its "packing loss." The idea is that the protons and neutrons are packed more tightly in the nucleus than when they are free. The packing loss of an element per unit of atomic mass is secured by dividing its packing loss by the number of units in its nucleus; this we can call its "packing factor." Obviously, the greater the packing factor of an element, the greater is the

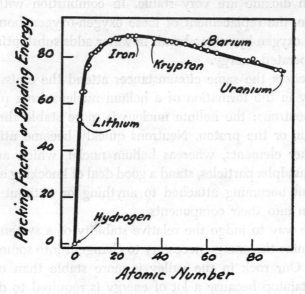

FIGURE 15. PACKING FACTOR

When protons and neutrons form atomic nuclei, they lose some of their mass as a result of the packing or binding of the particles in the nucleus. This loss per particle is the packing factor. It corresponds to the binding energy which is emitted, and its magnitude is shown for some interesting elements. The packing factor is given in hundredths of 1 per cent.

energy emitted in its formation, and the greater is its stability. It is as if the protons and neutrons were bound more tightly together in the nucleus as a result of the loss in mass and the emission of energy. Because of this idea, the emitted energy is often spoken of as the "binding energy" of the protons and neutrons in the nucleus.

Aston measured the relative masses of the various isotopes in his mass spectrometer and found that the packing factor of all the elements is not the same. So many regularities have already been discovered in the properties of the elements that it is not surprising to learn that even in their packing factor the elements show a regular behavior. The new regularity that Aston found is simple enough, but it is pregnant with meaning for every inhabitant of the earth. It lies at the very foundation of the process for the release of atomic energy.

Look at the packing factors of the elements shown in Figure 15. Hydrogen has a packing factor of 0, because its nucleus is just a single proton. The value for any other element is secured by subtracting its actual atomic weight from the sum of the weights of the protons and neutrons in its nucleus. This gives the packing loss, which when divided by the number of protons and neutrons in the nucleus gives the packing factor. For example, krypton-78 has 36 protons and 42 neutrons in its nucleus.

$$36 \times 1.0076 = 36.2736$$
$$42 \times 1.0089 = 42.3738$$
$$\text{sum} = 78.6474$$
$$\text{atomic weight of Kr-78} = 77.9262$$
$$\text{packing loss} = 0.7212$$

packing factor

referred to hydrogen = 0.0091, or 91 parts per 10,000

Clearly, krypton-78 has a loss of 91 parts per 10,000 for each of the 78 protons and neutrons that enter into the structure of its nucleus. It must be a stable nucleus indeed.

Figure 15 shows the packing factor of many of the elements. They lie on a curve that starts low at hydrogen, rises rapidly to reach a maximum at iron and nickel, and then decreases steadily to uranium. In other words, the light elements and the heavy elements of the Periodic Table have smaller packing factors than have the middle elements. Iron, which is at the top of the curve, has the largest packing factor. It is therefore the most stable element, whereas the lighter and the heavier elements are less stable than it is.

Look again at the sequence in Figure 15. Suppose it were possible to convert the elements into one another by rearranging their nuclear protons and neutrons. Then by starting at either end of the Periodic Table and constructing the elements in the middle, we could release energy, since we would be going from less stable to more stable elements. If we started with hydrogen we would combine smaller atoms to make larger ones. If we started with uranium, however, we would break large atoms into smaller ones. In both cases, the final mass would be less than the initial mass, and the difference would be given off as energy. Since we know that a trifling mass becomes tremendous energy, either process would yield vast amounts of energy.

Both procedures actually occur. The first type of process supplies the energy of the sun and the stars; it is discussed in detail in Chapter X, in conection with the so-called hydrogen bomb.

The second way of releasing energy in atomic transformations, from the heaviest elements, occurs on earth. For many years the only known course was through radioactivity. Remember that radium breaks up spontaneously to release helium and radon. The atomic weight of radium is 226, whereas the weights of helium and radon are 4 and 222, respectively. The large unstable nucleus of radium yields the smaller nuclei of helium and radon; mass is decreased because of the larger packing factors, and energy is therefore released. The energy is large, and we computed it earlier in our story.

Several other elements are naturally radioactive, but much less so than radium. The process, however, is the same. Smaller nuclei are formed, and energy is released, because of the packing-factor relations as shown in Figure 15.

Natural radioactivity is entirely spontaneous. The rate at which radium, uranium, thorium, and actinium normally break up to emit alpha particles, beta particles, and gamma rays is independent of man's activity and nothing we do has any influence on it. However, since 1939 we have learned another method of releasing energy by use of the change in packing factor from heavy-to-lighter elements. It consists in breaking the uranium nucleus up in such a way that the resulting nuclei are substantially lighter than the uranium nucleus and yield up vast amounts of energy. This is the method of the atomic bomb. It can be done at will and is entirely under the control of man.

3. ATOMS SPLIT AND RELEASE ENERGY: NUCLEAR FISSION

This is a good place to emphasize the fact that in all this work so far physicists were not concerned with the problem of releasing energy to produce atomic bombs. They were *SURE* concerned with understanding the structure of matter. They wished to explore the nucleus, to determine why protons that are positively charged, and should repel each other, can be in intimate stable contact in so small a space as the nucleus. They wanted to know what a neutron is and how it functions inside the nucleus.

Naturally they could not help speculating on occasions about the release of atomic energy. Some even wrote about the possibilities in the popular press; or at least they talked enough so that the news reporters wrote about the possibilities. However, the experiments that they performed were designed to answer the fundamental questions about matter and energy. The procedure was to bombard matter in bulk with alpha particles, with protons, with deuterons, and after 1932 with neutrons, and to see what happened.

In reviewing this work, one can see now that there were three kinds of result achieved. The first is quite simple and may be illustrated by the work of Cockcroft and Walton at the Cavendish Laboratory. They found that if a stream of protons at a relatively low velocity is directed against a film of the alkali metal lithium, there emerge alpha particles traveling at a very high velocity. It can be shown that for each proton that hits a lithium nucleus, two alpha particles appear.

The transformation is simple and straightforward. It is illustrated in Figure 16. A proton is a hydrogen nucleus $_1H^1$. Lithium is $_3Li^7$, its nucleus containing 3 protons and 4 neutrons. An alpha particle is the helium nucleus $_2He^4$ containing 2 protons and 2 neutrons. The process of their interaction may be written as

$$_3Li^7 + _1H^1 = _2He^4 + _2He^4$$

In reading this equation, first add the subscripts: 3 protons + 1 proton = 4 protons. Then add the superscripts: a mass of 7 + a mass of 1 = a mass of 8. Probably what first happens is that the lithium nucleus takes up the proton and for an instant it contains these 4 protons and 4 neutrons, making a mass of 8 with a charge of 4. This nucleus is so unstable that it breaks in two, forming 2 helium nuclei, each of mass 4 and charge 2.

Actually the two helium nuclei fly apart with great speed as if considerable energy were released in the readjustment of the unstable nucleus. That considerable energy is released can be shown in two ways. One is to determine the energy that the proton has before it hits the lithium atom, and the energy of the 2 alpha particles after they have been formed.

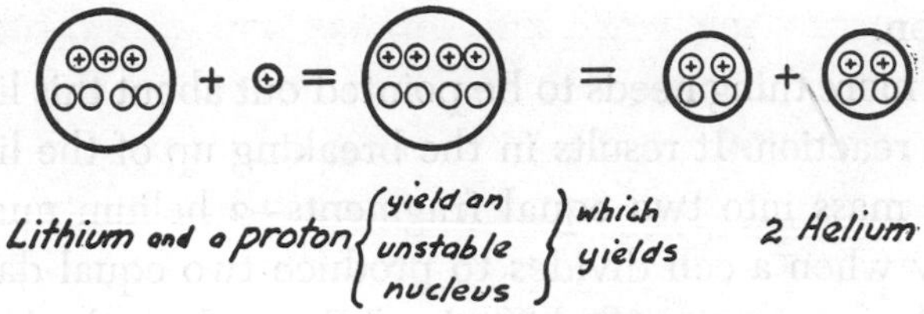

Lithium and a proton { yield an unstable nucleus } which yields   2 Helium

FIGURE 16. LITHIUM FISSION

A lithium nucleus after absorbing a proton splits into two helium nuclei with the release of energy.

This is done by measuring the speeds with which the particles travel and computing the energy by the usual equations of standard physics. The difference between the two velocities shows that considerable energy was released in the formation of the 2 alpha particles. After each collision the 2 alpha particles are released with a combined energy of 27.2 millionths of an erg for each atom of lithium.

The other way of showing the release of energy is to consider the loss of mass due to the changed packing factor. The lithium nucleus weighs 7.0165 and the proton weighs 1.0076; together they weigh 8.0241. An alpha particle weighs 4.0028, and two weigh 8.0056. Therefore the formation of 2 helium nuclei from lithium and hydrogen has resulted in the loss of 0.0185 unit of mass. This mass is responsible for the energy with which the 2 helium atoms are endowed, and by using Einstein's equation we can compute how much energy this is. The lost 0.0185 unit of mass actually weighs 3.07 x 10^{-26} gram, which when substituted in Einstein's equation equals 27.6-millionths of an erg per atom of lithium.

Notice how good an agreement the two methods give. In fact, for an experiment of this kind the agreement is almost perfect, and it demonstrates the complete equivalence of mass and energy. This, of course, is a proof of Einstein's equation.

One more thing needs to be pointed out about this lithium-proton reaction. It results in the breaking up of the lithium-proton mass into two equal fragments—2 helium nuclei. In biology when a cell divides to produce two equal daughter cells, the process is called "fission." By analogy the breaking of the nucleus into 2 equal helium nuclei may be called nuclear fission. Actually this term was not used till much later, when in 1939 the uranium nucleus was broken into two nearly equal fragments.

The interesting point at the moment is that when a proton and a lithium nucleus collide the result is 2 helium nuclei and considerable energy. Since the whole procedure is man-made, it might seem that this is a method for releasing atomic energy at will. And so it is; but not a very efficient method.

A little reflection shows why. Remember how small a nucleus is compared to the rest of the atom: the diameters are in the ratio of 1 to 10,000. Areas are proportional to the square of their diameters. The ratio of the diameters are as 1 is to 10,000. Therefore the cross-section areas are as 1 to 100,000,000—which means that in passing through a single lithium atom a proton has at best 1 chance in 100,000,000 of hitting the lithium nucleus. Actually, the chances are even fewer, because the proton and the lithium nucleus are both positively charged and repel each other. As the proton continues through the atoms, it hits electrons and becomes slowed down until it is finally stopped after having traversed about 100,000 atoms at best. Thus it has about 100,000 chances in 100,000,000 of hitting a lithium nucleus, or 1 chance in 1000. Even if the energy released is high, it hardly equals the energy required to get the protons moving, since at best only 1 in 1000 will hit a lithium nucleus. In short, this is a wasteful and inefficient method. The atomic energy is there, and it can be released, but only at the cost of a much greater expenditure of electrical energy.

4. RADIOACTIVE ATOMS ARE PRODUCED ARTIFICIALLY

In summarizing the action of atomic projectiles, I said that three kinds of result were achieved. The first is comparatively simple, like the fission of lithium just described. The second is somewhat more complex, and much more revolutionary.

Consider aluminum, the thirteenth element, with an atomic weight of 27. Its nucleus contains 13 protons and 14 neutrons, and it has no known isotope. When aluminum is hit with alpha particles, neutrons are emitted and a substance is formed whose nucleus has 15 positive charges and a mass of 30. This substance should be one whose nucleus contains 15 protons and 15 neutrons. The equation

$$_{13}Al^{27} + {}_2He^4 = {}_{15}P^{30} + {}_0n^1$$

bears this out; notice that the neutron is written as $_0n^1$ because it has a charge of 0 and a mass of 1.

Now a substance with 15 protons in its nucleus is the

fifteenth element in the Periodic Table, and this corresponds to phosphorus. Note, however, that the atomic weight of this newly formed substance is 30, whereas the atomic weight of phosphorus is 31, and it has no known isotope. These experiments were made by Frédéric Joliot and his wife, Irène Curie. The Joliot-Curies made chemical tests of this newly formed substance and found it actually to be phosphorus. Here then was a phosphorus lighter than common phosphorus, which had never been found in nature. It looked as though a new artificial isotope had been produced.

This indeed was exciting; but what was more exciting was that even while the chemical measurements and tests were being made the material seemed to vanish. In a quarter of an hour no phosphorus was left. And most exciting of all, as it disappeared, it was radioactive. It gave off the usual gamma rays, and in addition it gave off the elusive particle that had only recently been discovered, the positron. It will be recalled that this is the positive counterpart of the negative electron which Anderson had found in 1932. It has the trifling mass of the electron but its charge is positive instead of negative. The symbol for an electron is usually written as $_{-1}e^0$, which means 1 negative charge and no mass. The symbol for the positron is therefore $_1e^0$, or 1 positive charge and no mass.

The final product that appeared after the radioactive phosphorus disappeared was silicon, a well-known element, which combines with oxygen to make the main constituent of sand. Silicon is $_{14}Si^{30}$. Its formation from radiophosphorus may be conceived in terms of the following equation

$$_{15}P^{30} = {_{14}Si^{30}} + {_1e^0}$$

where $_1e^0$ is the positron ejected in the process.

Where does the positron come from? Look at Figure 17. Radiophosphorus has a nucleus of 15 protons and 15 neutrons. This is evidently an unstable arrangement in which there are too many protons. As a result, 1 positron is released, which may be conceived of as the positive charge from a proton. If the positive charge of a proton is removed, what remains is a neutral particle, a neutron. The transformation therefore is from a nucleus of 15 protons and 15 neutrons into one of 14 protons and 16 neutrons. This is a common

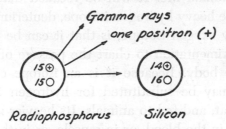

FIGURE 17. ARTIFICIAL RADIOACTIVITY

An unstable phosphorus nucleus spontaneously gives off gamma rays and one positron, and becomes converted into silicon. The gamma rays are powerful X rays, like those given off by natural radium.

isotope of silicon and was well known from the work of Aston.

The significant aspect of this discovery is not that one element has been transformed into another, because such transmutations had become relatively common by 1933. The revolutionary discovery is that there has been produced artificially a radioactive element like radiophosphorus, which so far as we know does not exist in nature.

Within a year, most of the easily available elements were tested in this way and practically all of them yielded radioactive isotopes. A whole new group of isotopes was thus artificially produced—isotopes that are radioactive. It is a curious quirk of destiny that artificial radioactivity should have been discovered by the daughter of the Curies, who had discovered the most potent source of natural radio-activity. In 1935 a Nobel Prize was awarded to the Joliot-Curies for this work.

The discovery that most elements can be produced in the form of radioactive isotopes opened the most wonderful pos-sibilities—more wonderful than atomic energy in their in-fluence on human life. It will be recalled that one of the virtues of the heavy hydrogen isotope, deuterium, as well as of the heavy oxygen isotope, is that it can be used in bio-logical experimentation to chart the passage of an element through the body. Because it is an isotope of hydrogen, deuterium may be substituted for hydrogen in water, in protein, in fat, and fed to animals. Its heavier mass betrays its presence in the blood, or in muscle, or in the urine, and when these are analyzed, the course of the substance con-taining the isotope may be followed in the body. This often involves killing the animal to remove the tissue. Moreover, it involves a fairly cumbersome analytical process.

The use of radioactive isotopes facilitates and extends this biological search enormously.

Before the war, only some stable isotopes of the lightest elements—such as ordinary hydrogen and deuterium, which differ in mass by a factor of 2—could be prepared by elaborate fractionation procedures. After the war, the electromagnetic separation plant in Oak Ridge, built to separate the isotope uranium-235 from uranium-238, was closed down, and some of its giant magnets were put to work separating isotopes of ordinary elements. Many stable isotopes, such as oxygen-18, or nitrogen-15, can now be purchased from the United

States Atomic Energy Commission at relatively moderate prices. Still, working with such isotopes remains a chore. One still needs a mass spectroscope to analyze the samples, and even cheap mass spectroscopes cost more than many a laboratory can afford. Above all, analysis still requires samples of the investigated material, which often cannot be secured without destroying the organism.

How much simpler and more elegant is working with radioactive elements! In the first place, the radioactive isotope always shows its presence by its radioactivity. No matter where it is, it steadily gives off positrons and gamma rays, which can be detected by the delicate means developed by physicists for their own atomic work. This can be done without killing the animal or destroying its organs.

In the second place almost any element may be prepared as a radioactive isotope, and the preparation of one is about as easy as another. Moreover, the radioactive isotope need not be separated for purposes of concentration; it can be directly produced by irradiation with neutrons of elements or chemicals used in the preparation of feed, or of material to be injected into animals or plants.

There is one possibility for using radioactive isotopes which is particularly fascinating. Some organs of the body have a special affinity for one element. For example, the thyroid gland in the neck has a special affinity for iodine, and the bones have a special affinity for phosphorus. We take iodine ordinarily in food and drinking water, and a large part of it goes to the thyroid gland to be stored as part of the material that the thyroid gland secretes. If the iodine were radioactive, a good deal of radioactivity could thus be concentrated in the thyroid gland. All tissues are sensitive to radioactivity because its gamma rays are powerfully destructive to living cells. However, cancer cells are much more sensitive to gamma rays than are ordinary normal cells. Therefore if there were cancer cells in the thyroid, the radioactivity would kill them more easily than it would kill normal cells, and the concentration could be so regulated that the cancer cells would be destroyed locally without injuring the normal thyroid cells. In the same way radioactive phosphorus would settle in the bones so as to destroy a bone cancer.

Successful treatment of malignant growth and other diseases of the thyroid gland with radioactive iodine has in fact been proved to be possible. In certain other cases—such as leukemia, a cancerous disease of blood corpuscles—other radioactive elements have proved of considerable help. Concentration of radioactive phosphorus in tumor tissue has been found useful to establish exact location and extension of tumors in the brain for operative purposes.

Radioactive cobalt, an isotope that has radiations similar to those of radium, can be produced artificially at much lower prices—and in much larger quantities—than natural radium. The Canadians showed the way by producing the first cobalt "irradiation bomb" in their atomic-energy plant at Chalk River, Ontario; Oak Ridge has followed suit. Radium therapy, which is still the greatest weapon short of the knife that we have against cancer—is thus becoming more powerful and accessible.

No miracle cure of cancer with radioactive elements has yet been found, and none is to be expected. The preference of the thyroid gland for iodine is an extreme case; in general, chemical elements, even those which have a tendency to concentrate in certain organs or tissues, scatter through the whole body in such strength that a dose needed to destroy a local tumor is likely to cause dangerous damage in other parts of the body.

However, what cannot be done with elements can perhaps be achieved with compounds. We do not yet know of a compound that would avoid healthy tissues and lodge exclusively in cells affected with malignancy, but the search for a compound or compounds of this type remains a legitimate and tempting object. It is the kind of speculation in which scientists often indulge and in the testing of which the most unexpected and most useful results may appear. Inherently it is no more improbable than many of the discoveries that have been recorded in the present story of atomic exploration.

New ways of medical diagnosis and treatment are only one of the many consequences of the sudden availability of radioactive isotopes of ordinary elements. For the investigation of normal physiological processes, the use of such isotopes as "tracers" to follow the path of different materials in the living organism, and to unravel the sequence of their chemical transformations, has rapidly become an indispensable tool. The weakly radioactive carbon isotope C-14, in particular, has proved a godsend to biologists. They only wish they had available similarly useful radioactive isotopes of oxygen and nitrogen, but no suitable isotopes of these elements exist. Hydrogen, which, with carbon, nitrogen, and oxygen, is the fourth main component of organic matter, has in addition to the stable isotope, deuterium (H-2), an artificial radioactive isotope, tritium (H-3), used to some extent in radioactive-tracer research.

In addition to medicine and biology, physics, chemistry, and engineering have also been much enriched by the possibility of using radioactive "tracers." The scope of this book does not permit us to go into this fascinating subject. We will merely give one simple example of the practical use of such tracers. A pipeline may carry one type of gasoline or oil for a certain length of time, then another, then a third, and so on. If every time the composition of the liquid is changed, a little radioactive isotope material is injected, its arrival at the destination will be announced by a radiation meter, such as a Geiger counter, giving the signal to switch the receptacles. The signal can be amplified to close and open the proper valves automatically.

The American atomic-energy installation at Oak Ridge began to sell radioactive isotopes at cost to medical, scientific, and industrial users in July 1947. Its sales have rapidly snowballed since. It has been joined by Canadian, French, and British atomic-energy plants; Russian research reports indicate that radioactive isotopes are available there, too.

But it is time to return from this excursion into the present to our historical narrative.

5. THE NEUTRON BECOMES EFFECTIVE

For our story the most effective particle used in the exploration of the structure of the nucleus is the neutron. The protons, deuterons, and alpha particles, whose actions against various elements have been described, are all positively charged particles. The proton is the nucleus of ordinary hydrogen, the deuteron is the nucleus of heavy hydrogen, and the alpha particle is the nucleus of helium. Because of their positive charge these particles are repelled by the nuclei of the elements against which they are directed. In order for them to collide with another nucleus and to enter it, they have to travel at great speeds. For years the cry had been for more and more speed, and for more powerful devices to send these particles hurtling at speeds closer and closer to the velocity of light.

Neutrons have the same mass as protons, but have no charge. Therefore they are not repelled by the positive nuclei of atoms against which they are moving, and can more easily come into contact with them. Soon after neutrons had been discovered by Chadwick in 1932, Enrico Fermi in Rome began to use them as missiles to send into the interior of the nucleus. As his work and that of his associates developed in Rome, it was duplicated and amplified by George B. Pegram and John R. Dunning at Columbia University in New York.

The results achieved were not dissimilar from the two types already described. New atoms were formed from other atoms, and radioactive isotopes of various elements were produced. However, the most important result of the work concerned the speed of neutrons. Because the other particles were being used at high speeds, when neutrons were first used they were also jacked up to high speeds. But it soon became obvious that this was not only unnecessary but even wrong. Slow neutrons were apparently much more effective than fast ones. In fact, neutrons that were so slow as to resemble in speed the ordinary random movements of atoms in a gas were found to be the most effective.

Such slow neutrons easily penetrate the nucleus. Then, if the combination of nucleus plus neutron is stable, the neutron simply remains in the nucleus and a new isotope of the original element is formed. But if the arrangement of nucleus plus neutron is unstable, it breaks up to liberate positrons or electrons and gamma rays, and to form a stable isotope of a different element; or the product may be a radioactive element that in its turn liberates positrons or electrons and gamma rays.

The slower the neutrons, the better for these purposes. Neutrons can be slowed down by letting them pass through paraffin or similar substances containing hydrogen or carbon, substances called "moderators," which we meet again later. The neutrons are slowed down because they are constantly bouncing against the protons of the hydrogen atoms or against the light and stable nuclei of the other moderators, and the collisions gradually dissipate their energies.

Many things were done with these very slow neutrons. But the one that belongs in our stream of history deals with the relation between neutrons and the heavy elements. Uranium is the last and heaviest natural element in the Periodic Table. Can one artificially produce still heavier elements? Fermi argued that if uranium were surrounded by slowly moving neutrons, some neutrons might enter the uranium nucleus, and possibly stay there. After some slight rearrangement of charges, involving the emission of a positron or an electron or of some small fragment, the result might be a new element, heavier than uranium. These possible elements were referred to as the transuranic elements.

The experiments that Fermi made for this purpose were encouraging. Electrons were liberated from uranium, but the results as a whole were not clear. The experiments were duplicated by others, but the results still remained puzzling. In fact, it was five years before these experiments were understood.

Such a delay is not uncommon in the history of science. However, this was 1934 and the state of the world may have contributed to the delay. First Germany, then Austria, and then Italy were being made uninhabitable for many scientists, who were forced to look for refuge in other countries. Forced migration is not conducive to creative thought—peace of mind is a prime requisite. By 1939, America, England, France, and Denmark had become the homes of an international galaxy of atomic physicists.

VI

ATOMIC BOMBS BECOME POSSIBLE

1. THE URANIUM ATOM SPLITS

Early in January 1939 the first clue was discovered that made the uranium-neutron experiments understandable. Otto Hahn and F. Strassmann, two chemists in Germany, had made chemical studies of the products of slow neutron action on uranium. Among the products they were astonished to find barium.

Remember that the uranium nucleus has 92 protons and 146 neutrons. Barium is $_{56}Ba^{138}$, and therefore has only 56 protons and 82 neutrons in its nucleus. Barium is so far from uranium in the Periodic Table that it does not seem sensible for it to appear as a product of neutron action on uranium. All previous experience leads one to expect the emission of a small fragment by uranium, perhaps an electron or a positron, and the appearance of some element immediately near the atomic weight of uranium. But what was barium doing here?

O. R. Frisch and Lise Meitner, in Copenhagen and Stockholm as refugees from Germany, had worked on uranium-neutron reactions; and as Lise Meitner meditated on this curious point, she had a revolutionary idea. Perhaps when uranium absorbs a neutron it splits into two roughly equal fragments. This would account for barium, which has about half the mass of uranium. She told this idea to her nephew and co-worker Frisch. They both discussed it with Niels Bohr, the director of the laboratory in Copenhagen and one of the great physicists, who was just about to leave for a stay at Princeton in order to discuss some theoretical problems with Einstein. Bohr arrived on January 16, 1939, and communicated Meitner's suggestion to his friends in Princeton and Columbia.

The effect of Bohr's news was immediate. As a biophysicist —one who applies physics to biology—working in my laboratory in the Physics Building at Columbia, I had some contact with the nuclear physicists who were working there at the time. It was fun to see the effect of Lise Meitner's suggestion. The weeks immediately following Bohr's arrival were filled with suppressed excitement, with lively speculation, and with critical experimentation. Everybody was working hard, thinking hard, and trying hard to appear nonchalant.

Meitner's suggestion was that when uranium absorbs a neutron it splits into two approximately equal fragments. Why all the excitement?

Uranium has 92 protons. When it splits, barium is formed. Barium has 56 protons, which leaves 36 protons for the other fragment. Look up number 36 in the Periodic Table; it is krypton. Now look up barium and krypton in the packing-factor diagram (Figure 15). They are among the elements with the highest packing factor. This means that when they are formed from uranium the final mass will be considerably less than the original mass, and a vast amount of energy will be liberated according to Einstein's equation for the conversion of mass into energy.

However, this was essentially no new story, and it should have been no cause for excitement. For instance, we learned that when lithium absorbs a proton it splits by perfect fission into two helium atoms and releases considerable energy as a result of the mass loss in terms of the packing factor. Moreover, we know that several such energy-releasing transformations have been investigated and that the whole situation is well understood. The energy release is certainly great, but as we have seen, it is useless for technical purposes. Much more energy is required to supply the protons or neutrons necessary to keep it going than can be got out of the reaction. The process stops the moment we stop supplying protons or neutrons.

Precisely here is where the excitement comes in. Look at Figure 18. Uranium-238 has 146 neutrons. Add to this number the one neutron that has caused fission. Barium-138 has 82 and krypton-83 47; together 129 neutrons. That leaves 18 neutrons to be accounted for. Even if some of these neutrons become converted to protons by the emission of beta rays, there is the possibility that several neutrons may remain free. It was the finding of these free neutrons that caused all the excitement.

When one neutron is absorbed by uranium, the latter breaks in two to give barium and krypton, with the release of lots of energy *and with the release of neutrons*. These released neutrons might then be absorbed by other uranium atoms, each of which would split into barium and krypton, and release energy and more neutrons. In this way one might get not only a lot of energy as the result of fission, but one or several neutrons to keep the process going as a chain reaction until all the uranium was changed into barium and krypton. The result would be the emission of truly enormous amounts of energy at the expense of just one original neutron, which started the first uranium atom on its path of fission. For the first time the efficient release of atomic energy on a large scale seemed possible.

The first job, however, was to determine whether Meitner's suggestion was true. If the uranium atom that has absorbed a neutron really splits in two, the resulting large fragments will fly apart with great energy. These heavy pulses of energy can easily be detected. Frisch looked for them, and found them almost immediately. Within a few days of one another

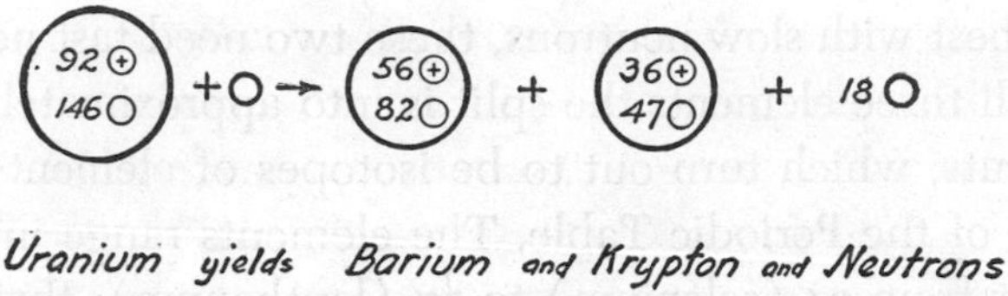

Uranium yields Barium and Krypton and Neutrons

FIGURE 18. NEUTRON RELEASE IN URANIUM FISSION

A uranium nucleus after absorbing a neutron splits into two fragments and releases the extra neutrons. This is the basic fact that makes an atomic bomb possible.

several groups of investigators here and abroad confirmed the results. Uranium fission was a reality.

The second job was to see whether neutrons are really emitted during fission. The idea that neutrons might be given off occurred independently to Joliot in Paris, to Fermi, and to Szilard, the last two both at Columbia University. With the help of colleagues they set about determining whether it is true. On March 8, 1939, H. von Halban, F. Joliot, and L. Kowarski sent their report for publication, and on March 16, 1939, H. L. Anderson, E. Fermi, and H. B. Hanstein, as well as L. Szilard and W. H. Zinn, sent their respective papers in for publication. All three groups of investigators by different methods found that neutrons are emitted during uranium fission. Atomic energy seemed around the corner.

2. WHICH URANIUM ISOTOPE FISSIONS?

The months following the demonstration of uranium fission with the emission of neutrons were full of such activity by many workers in different parts of the world that, in December 1939, when L. A. Turner summarized the year's work in the *Review of Modern Physics,* he covered about a hundred papers on fission. Two other elements, thorium and protactinium, were found to fission. However, whereas uranium works best with slow neutrons, these two need fast neutrons. With all three elements the split is into approximately equal fragments, which turn out to be isotopes of elements in the middle of the Periodic Table. The elements range in atomic number from 34 (selenium) to 57 (lanthanum); their packing factors are large, and therefore much energy is released during the splitting. Most of these fragments are radioactive, and therefore unstable; they emit electrons, neutrons, and gamma rays until they become stable.

In the particular case of uranium fission, the two fragments are only roughly equal: their atomic masses are about 140 and 90. In addition to barium and krypton, many other radioactive isotopes are produced, all of which emit gamma rays.

The most important thing about uranium fission that was discovered in 1939 concerns the uranium isotopes. Uranium has three naturally occurring isotopes. The main bulk of pure uranium—99.3 per cent of it—is $_{92}U^{238}$, which for short is written U-238. A small fraction, 0.7 per cent, is a lighter isotope, of atomic weight 235. It is $_{92}U^{235}$, and is written as U-235. Finally there is a trace of a still lighter isotope, $_{92}U^{234}$, to the extent of 0.006 per cent. Do all three isotopes of uranium undergo fission?

To answer this question it was necessary to separate the three isotopes and to test them individually for fission. We already know that the separation of isotopes is not easy. Moreover, the differences among the masses of U-238, U-235, and U-234 are relatively trifling; at best about 1 per cent. However, not much material is necessary for these tests; so A. O. Nier was able to separate them by a modification of Thomson's and Aston's method, which had originally demonstrated the existence of isotopes.

In the mass spectrograph uranium is converted into a stream of positive ions as in the old Geissler tube. The stream is passed through holes in the cathode and curved into an arc by means of a magnetic field. The lighter isotope curves more than the heavy one, and the two hit the photographic plate at different spots, as shown in Figure 13. Instead of letting the beams fall on a photographic plate as Thomson and Aston had done, Nier permitted them to become deposited on a surface upon which they could accumulate. Then each spot of isotope was separately tested with neutrons and the results observed and measured. It was quickly apparent that only one of the isotopes, namely U-235, underwent fission. Uranium-238 merely captured a neutron but did not undergo fission. Uranium-234 hardly enters the picture because of its trifling concentration.

Further investigation showed that U-235 can capture slow neutrons ever so much more easily than it can fast neutrons. For purposes of fission, slow neutrons are therefore best. On the other hand, the fast neutrons are captured by U-238, which they cannot fission.

This information was not a good augury for the release of atomic energy. Uranium-235 needs slow neutrons in order to fission. When U-235 fissions it releases fast neutrons.

Uranium-238, however, captures fast neutrons and does not fission. To maintain a chain reaction at least one of the neutrons released by U-235 must be captured by a nucleus of U-235. But the liberated fast neutrons are most easily captured by U-238, which they cannot fission. Moreover, in natural uranium there is 140 times as much U-238 as U-235. The fast neutrons released in the fission of U-235 will therefore be gobbled up by the U-238 nuclei before any of them can be absorbed by a U-235 nucleus to keep the chain reaction going.

There is an obvious way out of this fix: separate the isotopes so that you can have pure U-235 only. Then whatever neutrons are produced in its fission will have a good chance of being captured by U-235 nuclei without competition by U-238, and the chain reaction can have a good chance of going. Alas, this is an obvious way, but not an easy way. We have had experience with isotope separation before, from Aston's first attempts with neon-20 and neon-22 to Urey's successful hydrogen-deuterium separation, and the difficult oxygen-18 and oxygen-16 separation. The 1-per-cent difference in mass between U-235 and U-238 did not look propitious for easy isotope separation. Therefore, along this road, the release of atomic energy in terms of a chain reaction seemed possible but not likely.

3. NEWLY PRODUCED ATOMS THAT FISSION

The isotope U-238 absorbs fast neutrons but does not fission. What does it do? Nobody was entirely certain, but both evidence and theory seemed to indicate that the usual emission of small fragments might be occurring. Indeed in terms of some theoretical ideas that Bohr had formulated, one could guess what might be going on.

It is important to consider these guesses. Admittedly the theory of nuclear structure at that time was poor and limited. Admittedly, prediction in terms of it was more of an art than a science. However, in this particular case, the theory predicted correctly.

What can happen when U-238 absorbs a neutron? If the nucleus absorbs the neutron and retains it, we should get a new isotope of uranium, U-239, because the neutron would merely add to the mass of the nucleus and hence to its atomic weight. Such a first step may be written as

$$_{92}U^{238} + _{0}n^{1} = _{92}U^{239}$$

Add the subscripts for the charges and the superscripts for the masses.

According to theory, this is an unstable system with too many neutrons. A rearrangement of charges and masses will therefore take place and the nucleus will emit an electron. If a negative charge leaves the nucleus, this can come about if a neutron has emitted an electron to become a positively charged proton. The result is a nucleus with one less neutron but with one more proton than U-238. Uranium has 92 protons; the new nucleus will have a total of 93 protons. An element with 93 protons is a completely different element from uranium, and will occupy the next place in the Periodic Table.

This new element would be called neptunium, with its symbol Np, after the planet Neptune which lies beyond the planet Uranus, after which uranium was named. It would thus be one of the transuranic elements which Fermi and the others had speculated about beginning in 1934.

The theory also predicted that when neptunium is formed, there would be emitted not only an electron (written as $_{-1}e^{0}$)

but a fair amount of energy in the form of powerful X rays or gamma rays. The formation of neptunium Np from the transitory isotope U-239 can therefore be written as

$$_{92}U^{239} = \,_{93}Np^{239} + \,_{-1}e^0 + \text{gamma rays.}$$

The process does not stop here. According to the theoretical ideas about nuclear structure, Np^{239} should be relatively unstable. In a short while it too will emit from its nucleus an electron and powerful X rays. The emission of an electron from the nucleus again means the transformation of a neutron into a proton by the removal of a negative charge. From neptunium, which has 93 protons, we thus derive a nucleus with 94 protons, which constitutes still another new element.

No significant mass has been lost by the successive emission of the 2 electrons. Therefore the atomic weight is still 239. But the new element will be number 94 in the Periodic Table. It was named plutonium, after Pluto, the planet farthest out in the solar system. The equation for its production from neptunium is

$$_{93}Np^{239} = \,_{94}Pu^{239} + \,_{-1}e^0 + \text{gamma rays.}$$

The final prediction from theory is perhaps the most significant. It says that the new element plutonium, Pu-239, is relatively stable and that it will absorb slow neutrons preferentially and undergo fission much as U-235 does.

If these theoretical predictions are true, then the absorption of a neutron by U-238 will yield the new element plutonium, Pu-239, which is just as fissionable as U-235 but which can be secured in much larger quantities because of the greater concentration of its parent, U-238, in natural uranium. Moreover, since plutonium is a chemically different element from uranium, there will be no difficulty in separating it from uranium after it is formed, and purifying it.

A mass of plutonium can then be prepared in which to start a chain reaction. A single neutron supplied from an outside source will be absorbed by a plutonium nucleus. It will fission into two flying fragments with the emission of heat, gamma rays, and several neutrons. These neutrons will be absorbed by plutonium nuclei, each of which will fission, emit energy and more neutrons, and this chain process will go on until all the mass of plutonium has been converted into fission fragments and enormous energy.

Thus theory at the end of 1939. And thus fact in 1945.

4. CAN ATOM SPLITTING BE KEPT UP?

All that I have written up to now, and much more, was common knowledge among those all over the world who were capable of understanding it. Much of it is to be found in elementary textbooks; all of it is available in advanced textbooks and in professional journals of physics. Far from being secretive, atomic physicists were a gregarious international group, and communicated information and ideas to one another by word of mouth, by mail, by telephone, and even by transatlantic cable. Everybody knew everybody else and everyone knew everything. Ideas were circulated freely, and were discussed critically. As a result enthusiasm ran high and science progressed rapidly.

The year 1939 saw the termination of this free exchange. In September the Germans invaded Poland, and Europe was at war. Many scientists reluctantly abandoned their regular work and turned to the problems of war. Some in the United

States and in England began to think of the military possibilities of a uranium or plutonium chain reaction in the production of atomic energy.

The mere computations were terrifying. The reader who has gone so far in this story can make these computations for himself. He knows the packing factors of uranium and of its fission products barium and krypton. The difference is the mass lost in the fission process, which will be given off as energy in terms of Einstein's equation. The percentage decrease in mass is the same for an atom as for a pound. Therefore he can calculate what would happen with a pound of U-235 pure, if we were to get it free from its isotope U-238. If a chain reaction could become established and all the atoms in the pound of U-235 be fissioned, the energy produced would be over 400 billion billion ergs, or in common units, 12,000,000 kilowatt-hours.

If this energy were released slowly under control it would furnish the electric current that keeps 12 million 100-watt lamps going for a 10-hour day, or about enough to illuminate all the homes in New England for an evening.

If, however, it were released quickly, say in a fraction of a second, it would have the explosive force of about 10,000 tons of TNT. Since there are 2000 pounds in a ton, this is a factor of 20,000,000, and says that pound for pound, U-235 could yield an explosive force 20,000,000 times more powerful than TNT. If only 10 per cent of the atoms in a pound of U-235 were to fission, it would be 2,000,000 times as powerful as TNT; or even if only 1 per cent of the atoms in the pound of U-235 were to fission, it would still be equivalent to 200,000 times the explosive force of TNT. Clearly a new order of explosive force was possible, and the sleep of those who made these calculations was not easy.

This is very nice on paper. But in reality no one had established such a chain reaction. No one had separated more than a hundred-millionth of a gram of U-235; this was a microscopic speck on a slide and was used to test which uranium isotope undergoes fission. A pound of U-235, indeed! One had better stay with ordinary uranium with its three isotopes and see what can be done about the possibilities of a chain reaction.

The basic fact is that an atom of U-235 when it absorbs a slow neutron undergoes fission and liberates fast neutrons. In ordinary uranium many things can then happen, and a chain reaction will result only if several factors are just right.

The first is fission capture. Uranium-235 will fission when it captures a slow neutron. Will U-235 fission if it captures a fast neutron? It is quite likely. But we cannot know, because in natural uranium there is 140 times as much U-238 as U-235 and it captures all the fast neutrons without undergoing fission.

Can one slow down the neutrons produced in the fission of U-235 so that they will be captured mainly by other atoms of U-235? One did not know, but there were ideas as to how it could be done. Light elements such as helium, carbon, beryllium, and heavy hydrogen do not absorb neutrons easily but bounce them back and therefore slow them down. These are the moderators that Fermi and Pegram and Dunning had been using all along to produce very slow neutrons. Could one of these moderators be mixed with uranium so as to slow down the fast neutrons emitted by fission and in this way supply the slow neutrons to be captured by U-235 for further fission?

The second factor concerns purity. Most substances capture neutrons and do not fission. Any impurities present in uranium would absorb the emitted neutrons and they would be wasted. Therefore the uranium has to be very pure. Also any moderators for slowing down the neutrons must be pure. The degree of purity is not trivial. Computations showed that impurites cannot be present as more than 1 part per million. Could one purify uranium or any of the moderators to this extent?

A third factor is the matter of neutron escape. Take a lump of uranium and send in a slow neutron. It hits a U-235 atom, which undergoes fission and releases some neutrons. If the lump is small, these neutrons have a good chance of getting out through the surface of the lump into the air before they are absorbed by some other U-235 atom. Once they get out they are lost, and if more get out than are captured, there will be no chain reaction.

5. THE CRITICAL SIZE OF AN ATOMIC BOMB

There is an amusing and vital point here. In a piece of uranium the loss of neutrons is through the surface, whereas the capture of neutrons is by the mass of the material.

Simple geometry tells us that the volume of a sphere varies as the cube of its radius, while the surface of a sphere varies as the square of the radius. Therefore as a lump of uranium increases in size, its surface does not increase as rapidly as its volume or mass. In other words, the larger the lump is, the less surface it offers per unit mass. Since the loss is through the surface, and capture is by the mass, the larger the lump the greater is the chance of the released neutrons staying inside the mass to be captured by U-235 for fission purposes.

The next question is how large a lump must be so that most of the neutrons get caught, and are not lost through the surface. The critical mass will be that chunk of uranium just large enough so that more neutrons will be retained than are lost. A piece of uranium smaller than this critical mass can never give a chain reaction. A piece larger than the critical mass will do so if all other factors are right.

What is the critical size? This depends on the range of the neutrons in uranium. How far can a neutron go before it is captured? This was known only very roughly, and therefore the critical mass was known only roughly. The available measurements indicated a value between 2 and 200 pounds of U-235 as the critical mass.

Most of the information on the fission of uranium had been secured from specks of the material less than a millionth of a gram in weight. (In case the reader has forgotten, 28 grams make 1 ounce.) A critical mass of U-235 weighing between 2 and 200 pounds was just fantastic. No one had ever seen more than a few grams of uranium as a metal all in one place. It was used in making ceramics and steel, but in the most trifling concentrations.

Uranium constitutes between 40 and 90 per cent of the mineral pitchblende, and pitchblende was known to be available in Czechoslovakia, Canada, and Belgian Congo. Other, less rich uranium minerals were known to occur in the Colorado plateau and in many other localities on the earth, including Asiatic Russia. To secure 200 pounds of U-235 would mean first processing tons of pitchblende to get the uranium metal pure, and then separating the isotope U-235 from the 140-times-more-prevalent U-238 in it. To work with the isotope mixture as it is plus a moderator to slow the neutrons would mean tons of the purified metal.

A similar situation existed with regard to the moderators for slowing the neutrons. Possible moderators were beryllium, heavy water, and carbon; and tons of these would be required just to try out a chain reaction.

Beryllium is a common element, and several hundred pounds of the metal were being produced yearly in the United States. It was not very pure, because there was no need for it.

Heavy water exists normally, as we learned earlier, about 1 part in 5000 parts of ordinary water. Heavy water can be concentrated by several means, and a large-scale factory for producing a few hundred quarts a year existed in Norway. In the United States a few quarts had been prepared, mostly for scientific purposes.

Carbon would be an excellent moderator. It was being produced in relatively large amounts—many hundreds of tons per year—as graphite for lubricating purposes. It was not purified to the necessary extent, but it was at least available and could probably be purified. Its use was suggested very early by Szilard and Fermi.

Suppose one could get enough pure uranium and enough pure moderator to exceed the critical mass and to establish a chain reaction. It might get out of hand. It might blow up. Even if it did not blow up, it might give off enough radio-activity and X rays to devastate a whole area and make it uninhabitable for months. Therefore one had to look for efficient neutron absorbers—substances that capture neutrons but do not themselves change very much. These could be inserted into the mass so as to control the reaction. A few such absorbing substances were known. One is cadmium, a metal belonging to the ancient triad of cadmium, zinc, and mercury. Others were suspected of being absorbers and would have to be tried out. There seemed to be plenty of work before a chain reaction could be attempted.

VII

ATOMIC BOMBS CAN BE MADE

1. TWO-BILLION-DOLLAR GAMBLE

In January 1939, Frisch and Meitner had suggested uranium fission. In a few weeks it had been tested and found true. In a few more weeks most of the computations and ideas just described had been gone through by several people, notably by Szilard and by Fermi at Columbia. The military possibilities had become clear, particularly to a small group of physicists centering around Szilard and including Eugene Wigner, Edward Teller, Victor F. Weisskopf, and Fermi. These were all European scientists who had found refuge in this country from Nazi and Fascist persecution, and they recognized the war clouds in Europe early. Most of our American-born scientists did not think in political and military terms quite so soon as the spring of 1939.

This small group, with the help of Bohr, immediately tried to organize a voluntary stop to the publication of critical data. American and British physicists entered the agreement, but Joliot refused, apparently because of a small paper that had been published before all American physicists had accepted voluntary censorship. Therefore the year 1939 saw the flood of papers on fission that has already been referred to. Actually, voluntary censorship did not begin until April 1940. This voluntary censorship was completely successful and went on for several years, long before any secrecy was established by the military.

It was obvious that to get on with the chain-reaction problem large amounts of materials would be required, more than any university laboratory can afford. Since the military implications were compelling it was logical to turn to the government for help.

In March 1939 Pegram arranged a conference between Fermi and representatives of the Navy Department. The Navy expressed interest and asked to be kept informed.

Goaded by the possibilities and by the delays, Szilard and Wigner conferred with Einstein in July and decided to appeal to President Roosevelt. This appeal was finally made in the fall by Alexander Sachs, who carried a letter from Einstein with a memorandum by Szilard, and who explained to the President the nature of the problem and the necessity for financial support of the work. The President appointed a committee of three—one civilian, one Navy ordnance man, and one Army ordnance man—to look into the matter and to advise him.

This committee met several times and listened to evidence; and it made recommendations. Finally on February 20, 1940, the first funds from the Army and Navy were transferred to Columbia for the purchase of critically necessary materials. Total transferred—$6000.

The committee met again on April 28, 1940, and listened to reports of progress. By this time research had demonstrated that of the three uranium isotopes only U-235 would fission, and that slow neutrons are more effective than fast ones. Also the measurements on graphite at Columbia had shown that it would be a good moderator. Above all, news had reached various scientists that a large section of one of the Kaiser Wilhelm Institutes—the greatest research organization in Germany—had been set aside for work on uranium. A special advisory group that met in June 1940 reported to the committee that $100,000 worth of uranium and graphite was required to try out a chain reaction, and that $40,000 would be necessary to make the fundamental measurements.

Before it could act on these recommendations the committee ceased to function. In June 1940 the whole problem of civilian scientific aid to the military had been given to a newly organized group, the National Defense Research Committee (NDRC), and a reconstituted Uranium Committee had been set up in its framework. It was composed almost entirely of civilian scientists. It had some funds, and it arranged contracts between NDRC and various research institutions.

The first contract was signed November 8, 1940, and assigned to Columbia University. It ran from November 1, 1940, to November 1, 1941, and was for $40,000. Other contracts were soon granted. During the year one went to Columbia for Urey to separate uranium isotopes by the centrifuge method, which is described later in this chapter. Other contracts went to Princeton, Cornell, Chicago, and other universities and research institutions. By November 1941 sixteen such projects were under way. Total appropriation: $300,000.

There is little point in recounting the detailed administrative history of what happened subsequently. However, it is desirable to give a general picture of the events. For a long time the military was not impressed; it was willing to go along, and it supplied some funds. The problem was in the hands of civilian scientists. These were of two kinds. One was a small group of enthusiastic and imaginative insiders who were frantic and frustrated by delays. The other was a larger but much less excited group who wanted to go from one established point to the next and to whom the amounts of money involved seemed large and the chances very small. Actually, in the early days of NDRC, the amounts of money allocated to other researches were larger than for the uranium work; but the other researches seemed immediate in application, whereas the atom bomb seemed remote indeed.

The British had of course been thinking along lines similar to ours. Chadwick was certain that a bomb of U-235 could be made. As a whole the British group wanted to concentrate on the separation of U-235 from U-238 by diffusion on the principle that I have already described for neon-20 and neon-22 separation. Moreover, Bretscher and Feather had suggested the possibility of plutonium, though the British never pursued it, probably because of their limited manpower. The British naturally had thought of moderators for slowing the neutrons emitted by the fission of U-235, in order to attempt a chain reaction with ordinary uranium. They had even decided on heavy water as the moderator and had begun to design a plant for this purpose.

During 1940 and 1941 there had been both formal and informal exchanges of information between the British and our own scientists. In general the British scientists were more optimistic about atomic-bomb production than our official NDRC advisers, and they supported our small but active group of enthusiasts.

One of the critical events of the early days was the journey to England in the fall of 1941 by Urey and Pegram to see at first hand what the British uranium situation was. Pegram and Urey brought back much information, but, most important, they carried back a sense of urgency which even in the cold report communicated itself to the administrative group here.

The gist of all this information was conveyed to President Roosevelt and Vice-President Wallace. As a result the decision was made in December 1941, just before Pearl Harbor, to broaden the uranium program, to provide funds from a special source, and to work closely with the British. Thus ended the year 1941, with us in the war, and with some real prospects for the uranium work.

The changed psychological situation was important. Even in 1940 Szilard, Fermi, and Wigner did not need to be convinced of the possibility of an atomic bomb. But many other people had been either lukewarm or frankly skeptical. By the end of 1941, the idea had been sufficiently talked about so that a number of administratively powerful scientists had become familiar with it and with its meaning for the war. They decided that the uranium project had to be pushed vigorously.

2. CAN URANIUM FISSION MAINTAIN ITSELF?

During 1940 and 1941 material was being purified and accumulated to test the possibilities of a chain reaction. This work was under the general leadership of Pegram at Columbia with Fermi and Szilard in actual charge. In the early months of 1941 a sufficient amount of extremely pure carbon in the form of graphite had been prepared to make a column 3 by 3 by 8 feet. By placing a neutron source at the bottom of this pile, and measuring instruments in various positions inside, one was able to study the properties of the neutrons as they traveled through carbon.

As a result a most important new idea was developed, which in practice came to be called a "lattice pile."

A lattice pile is essentially a pile of graphite bricks arranged with small spaces between them. At regular locations equally distributed throughout the pile are placed small pieces of ordinary uranium metal. This sharp separation of graphite as moderator from uranium as neutron producer has a special virtue. The fast neutrons emitted by the fission of U-235 leave the small uranium lumps easily, but before

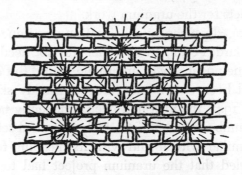

FIGURE 19. LATTICE PILE

Bricks of graphite separate small lumps of ordinary uranium. In this way fast neutrons released by U-235 in any one lump must pass through a lot of moderating graphite (carbon) before reaching another lump of uranium. This passage through the carbon slows down the neutrons, so that they may be captured by U-235 in another lump.

they reach the next lump of uranium in the pile, they must go through a given thickness of graphite carbon and therefore are slowed down so that they will be absorbed by the U-235 atoms and cause them to fission. Figure 19 illustrates the idea.

By July 1941 the graphite-uranium lattice had reached a cube 8 by 8 by 8 feet in size and contained 7 tons of purified uranium. This pile was located in the basement of Schermerhorn Hall at Columbia. At the bottom of the cube was a radium-beryllium mixture, which served as a source of neutrons.

The object of the pile was to determine what became known as the multiplication factor. It will be recalled that several circumstances have to be just right in order for a chain reaction to occur. Suppose these factors balanced so well that, for every atom of U-235 that fissions one of the emitted neutrons will finally be absorbed by another atom of U-235 and cause it to fission. If this goes on, each atom that fissions produces another atom that fissions, and so on.

Let us start with 100 U-235 atoms, each of which has received a neutron from the outside source. If as a result of the correct balance of factors the fission of these 100 atoms ultimately results in 100 other U-235 atoms getting a slow neutron each so that they can fission and produce a neutron each, and so on, then the multiplication factor is 1.00, and the chain reaction will just maintain itself. If the factors are such that from the neutrons emitted by the original 100 atoms, 105 neutrons manage to survive and get to U-235 atoms, then 105 atoms will fission. The multiplication factor is now 1.05, and the reaction will slowly increase in speed. However, if from the neutrons emitted by the original 100 atoms of U-235 only 95 manage to be captured by other U-235 atoms, the reaction cannot maintain itself. Its multiplication factor will be 0.95, and the reaction will stop soon.

In September 1941 the pile was large enough to test, and Fermi reported the multiplication factor to be 0.87. In other words, under the conditions of the pile the chain reaction could not be sustained. However, even though the value was less than 1.00, it was not too far from 1.00, and Fermi believed that it could be increased by improving the purity of the components, the size of the pile, and the arrangement of the substances in the lattice. But could the multiplication factor ever become greater than 1.00? No one knew for certain, and this remained the basic question. In fact, it was not answered until more than a year later.

3. NEWLY CREATED ATOMS FOR BOMBS

While this was going on at Columbia other groups in other universities were investigating different possibilities. The most important of these was at the University of California under the general leadership of E. O. Lawrence and the immediate direction of E. Segré. This group concentrated on the problem of what happens to U-238 when it captures fast neutrons. We know what the theory is; but is it really true that after U-238 absorbs a neutron it gives off an electron and becomes $_{93}Np^{239}$, the new element neptunium? And does this new element give off still another electron from its nucleus to become $_{94}Pu^{239}$, the new element plutonium? And is plutonium just as fissionable as U-235?

The importance of the reactions is apparent when we recall two points. One is that U-238 constituted 99.3 per cent of ordinary purified uranium. If U-238 can be converted into fissionable material resembling U-235, then the mere fact that 140 times as much of it is available is a great asset. The other point is that plutonium is a different chemical species from uranium. After formation it can be separated from the unchanged uranium by relatively simple chemical procedures.

Before the end of the year 1941 the California group had established that U-238 by the capture of one neutron does go through neptunium to form plutonium, and that plutonium is actually fissionable with slow neutrons just like U-235.

This had been accomplished with about one millionth of a gram of uranium.

Ten years later, the leaders of this research, the physicist Edwin Mattison McMillan and the chemist Glenn Seaborg received a Nobel Prize for their achievement. Seaborg and his co-workers had in the meantime gone on and built up, by the same procedure, the artificial elements 95 (americium), 96 (curium), 97 (californium), and 98 (berkelium). A few years earlier, the discovery of fission had been recognized by a Nobel Prize award to Otto Hahn.

The actual demonstration of the formation of plutonium and of its fissionable character presented the steering uranium committee with alternative paths to follow. One was to separate the isotope U-235 from U-238 and prepare it in sufficient quantities for a bomb. The other was to make plutonium from U-238, and to prepare *it* in sufficient quantities for a bomb.

Under normal conditions one would evaluate the relative chances of reaching the goal by the two paths, choose one, and concentrate all efforts on it. These, however, were not normal times, and both paths had to be explored and developed.

Similar situations arose all through the next four years. Whenever two or more possibilities existed, all of them had to be developed.

4. THREE OTHER WAYS TO GET BOMB MATERIAL

Our story has now ceased to describe a single development that like a continuously numbered route on a road map can be followed across the country. Instead it depicts a land actively traversed in many directions by several groups of explorers. All are at work simultaneously. To follow it we travel for short stretches on one route, then another, and then a third, and only occasionally do we get an air view of the whole activity.

Let us consider the separation of U-235 from U-238. These are isotopes and cannot be separated by means that depend on chemical differences. Only by their slight difference in weight of 3 parts in 235 can they be isolated from each other. This path of physical separation branches into three forks.

The first is magnetic, and is by means of the mass spectroscope. Remember Thomson's first separation of neon-20 and neon-22 at the cathode end of a Geissler tube. Remember also Aston's much enlarged and amplified apparatus with which he first showed the existence of isotopes in bunches. The idea is to ionize an element and make a stream of ions that then passes near a powerful magnet. Because of any difference in charge or mass the elements in the stream will be spread out and deflected to different extents, and may be caught in different places. Normally, they merely collect in different spots of a photographic plate to record their presence for the investigator to measure.

All this can be done for uranium. It can be vaporized and ionized in a partial vacuum. As a positive ion stream coming through the holes in the cathode it can then be spread by a powerful magnet into two streams, one of U-235 and the other of U-238, as shown in Figure 20. Then instead of falling on a photographic plate the U-235 beam passes through a hole and is deposited in a receptacle beyond the hole, while U-238 remains behind and is deposited separately.

The California group worked on this and by December 1941 they reported that a millionth of a gram of U-235 reasonably free from U-238 could be separated per hour. At the rate of one-millionth of a gram of U-235 per hour, it would take 450,000,000 hours to deposit 1 pound. This is roughly 60,000 years. One could hardly wait for this procedure to furnish material.

Could the separation be done on a large scale? It probably could. However, special machinery would have to be designed and built. Pilot plants would have to be constructed

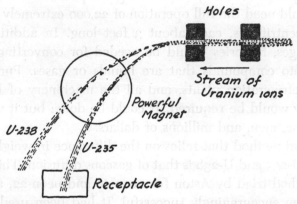

FIGURE 20. MAGNETIC SEPARATION OF URANIUM ISOTOPES

The powerful magnet deflects the lighter isotope more than it does the heavier, and enables the lighter isotope U-235 to be accumulated in the pure state free of U-238. Compare Figure 13.

and tested, and a new industry would have to be established. It would take much money and many men. We were at war, and both materials and scientific men were at a premium.

A second method of physically separating U-235 and U-238 depends on the centrifuge. A centrifuge is a fancy name for a cream separator. When milk is whirled around and around in a cream separator the lighter part, which is the cream, rises to the top, whereas the heavier part, the milk, sinks to the bottom. Could one whirl uranium in a gaseous or liquid form around and around so that the difference of 3 parts in 238 by weight would bring the lighter U-235 to the top and leave the U-238 on the bottom?

Toward the end of 1941, the most careful experiments under the general direction of Urey at Columbia showed that it could be done. Calculations from the theoretical developments of this idea by Karl Cohen give some notion of the magnitude of the process. To get 2 pounds of U-235 a day would need the full operation of 22,000 extremely high-speed centrifuges, each about 3 feet long. In addition to centrifuges, factories would be needed for converting uranium into compounds that are liquids or gases. Pumping units, refrigeration plants, and all the machinery of heavy industry would be required. It could be done; but it would take time, men, and millions of dollars.

A third method that relies on the difference in weight between U-235 and U-238 is that of gaseous diffusion. This was the method tried by Aston for neon-20 and neon-22, and it had been encouragingly successful. It had been used later for separating the isotopes of the green gas chlorine.

The first step is to convert uranium to a compound normally a gas. This step is simple because a compound of uranium and fluorine is such a gas. The gas is uranium hexafluoride, UF_6, the heaviest of gases. It may interest the reader to know that for the sake of secrecy uranium was called Tube-Alloy by the British. The gas was therefore referred to by them as Tube-Alloy hexafluoride. If this gas is pumped through tiny holes in a plate, the gas molecules containing the lighter isotope U-235 will go through a little faster than the ones made with the heavier U-238 isotope. Once the gas has gone through the barrier, it will be slightly richer in U-235 than in U-238. To make it still richer, it can be passed through another barrier, and then through another barrier, and so on until a gas very rich in U-235 is obtained.

Experiments and computations at Columbia showed that to get 2 pounds of U-235 per day would need about 5000 stages of diffusion, one after the other. The barrier plates through which the gases would be pumped would have an area equal to several acres. A first estimate of the cost of such a plant was over 20 million dollars.

Still a fourth method was tested at the Bureau of Standards in Washington. It was a variant of the diffusion method, and work on it was continued at the Naval Research Laboratory. It looked quite promising. A pilot plant was built but was later abandoned. I merely mention it to show the variety of ideas available.

5. MONEY BEGINS TO FLOW

We are now at the end of 1941. Fermi had found a multiplication factor of 0.87 with the lattice pile at Columbia. At California plutonium had been demonstrated chemically and its fissile properties confirmed. The California group had even suggested that if a chain reaction were established in the U-235 of a lattice pile made up of ordinary uranium and graphite, the excess neutrons could be used to convert U-238 to plutonium-239. In this way the pile would manufacture plutonium under its own power. At least three methods of separating U-235 had been worked out. They had been tested on a small scale and estimates had been made of the cost of setting them up in large-scale production.

It was at this moment that Urey and Pegram came back from England and brought with them the sense of urgency that prevailed there. The Germans had overrun Denmark and had conquered Norway. Holland and Belgium had fallen and France had been defeated. It was after Dunkerque.

In Norway the Germans had immediately taken possession of the only large factory in the world for the production of heavy water. What did they want with heavy water except to use it as a moderator for slowing down neutrons in a uranium chain reaction? It will be recalled that we had considered heavy water for this purpose, but had turned to graphite as a moderator. However, heavy water was being produced by Urey in case it proved necessary. The British had decided to use heavy water, and so had the French. In fact, Joliot's last act before leaving Paris had been to send to England the several quarts of heavy water that had been slowly accumulated in France.

By this time too the scientific effort of the war had become enormous. The original National Defense Research Committee (NDRC) had become the much larger Office of Scientific Research and Development (OSRD), headed by Vannevar Bush and composed of two divisions with many sections each. These were civilian organizations run by scientists, who studied the problems and allocated funds in the form of contracts to universities and research institutions for their investigation.

In November 1941 the Uranium Section of NDRC had become Section S-1 of OSRD, and in December 1941 an all-out effort was decided upon. The section was organized into a planning board of scientists, and a group of three scientific program chiefs. In addition, Bush appointed a separate planning board that would be responsible for the technical and engineering aspects of the work, for procurement of materials, and for construction of pilot plants and full-size production plants.

Naturally, political policy was not the province of scientists and engineers. The Top Policy Group concerned with such decisions consisted of the President (F. D. Roosevelt), the Vice-President (H. A. Wallace), and the Secretary of War (H. L. Stimson), the Chief of Staff (G. C. Marshall), the Director of OSRD (V. Bush), and the Director of NDRC (J. B. Conant). At a meeting of the Top Policy Group in December 1941, at which Wallace, Stimson, Bush and Budget Director H. L. Smith were present, it was decided "that OSRD should press as fast as possible on the fundamental physics and on the engineering planning, and particularly on the construction of pilot plants." Bush estimated the cost of this phase of the work as about 5 million dollars. Bush also suggested that the Army take over when full-scale construction began, and requested that a competent Army officer be assigned early to learn about the problem.

Things really began to happen then. The three program chiefs were E. O. Lawrence of California, A. H. Compton of Chicago, and H. C. Urey of Columbia, who vigorously pursued programs that are described presently. With relatively minor administrative changes the scientific and engineering development work continued under OSRD until the spring of 1943, when it was taken over by the Manhattan District.

In August 1942 the problem had reached the point where large-scale production was clearly called for. Following Bush's advice, production was taken on by a new organization formed by the Corps of Engineers of the Army. This was labeled DSM (Development of Substitute Materials) and was known officially as the Manhattan District of Army Engineers, or, colloquially, as the Manhattan Project. It was first set up by Colonel J. C. Marshall, and in September 1942

Major General L. R. Groves was placed in charge. This organization later took over the scientific research and development as well. In January 1947 it was superseded by the civilian Atomic Energy Commission.

6. URANIUM FISSION MAINTAINS ITSELF

Regardless of all the superorganization and regardless of all the urgency, by January 1942 no chain reaction had yet been established. This was merely because time and apparatus were required to purify the requisite amounts of materials and to study the best way of making a pile. Whatever was done on the rest of the program had to be done in the faith that a chain reaction would proceed when the critical mass of material was accumulated and properly arranged.

One of Compton's first acts after the reorganization was to move much of the Columbia group to the University of Chicago. This included Fermi, Szilard, Anderson, and Zinn. The new place in Chicago was called the Metallurgical Laboratory and its spreading growth occupied all the physics and chemistry laboratories of the university and soon expanded beyond them.

The job of highest priority for the group was the chain reaction. All during 1942 graphite and uranium were procured and purified. Experimental lattice piles were constructed to learn the properties of the materials and the piles. By the fall enough materials were available to have another try at a lattice pile that would yield a self-sustaining chain reaction.

The pile was constructed under the squash courts in the stadium of the University of Chicago. As before, bricks of graphite were set up between which lumps of uranium were placed at regular distances. One precaution was taken. Removable rods of cadmium were inserted in various parts of the pile. Cadmium absorbs neutrons and is not changed by them. A rod or plate of cadmium serves as a shield to retard neutron transmission from point to point, and thus serves to control the speed of the reaction. And a good thing it was to have these retarding rods, because the pile worked better than its producers expected. By December 1, 1942, everything at the squash courts was ready to go.

By a curiously dramatic coincidence this was precisely the time when a reviewing committee arrived at Chicago to evaluate the progress of the Metallurgical Laboratory. The most decisive moment in the scientific history of the whole development occurred on December 2, 1942, when the pile was started. It maintained itself. For the first time in the history of the world, human beings had initiated a self-sustaining nuclear chain reaction.

VIII

ATOMIC BOMBS ARE MADE

1. SMALL-SCALE PRODUCTION OF THE NEW ATOM
PLUTONIUM

The construction of a self-sustaining chain-reacting lattice pile solved two problems at once. First, it showed that a U-235 chain reaction is possible; therefore atomic energy from the packing loss in the nucleus is available for technical purposes if released slowly, or for a bomb if released rapidly. Second, it showed that plutonium, which behaves like U-235, can be manufactured in the pile.

When a lattice pile is self-sustaining it means that each fission of a U-235 atom produces neutrons of which at least one reaches another U-235 atom that fissions and continues the chain. But as we learned before, the fission of a U-235 atom produces more than one neutron. What happens to the other neutrons? These are captured by U-238, which is converted into neptunium and finally into plutonium with the emission of radioactivity. In other words a pile is an atomic factory to convert U-238 into Pu-239. The medieval philosopher's stone had finally been realized on a mass-production basis.

From then on, plutonium production became essentially an engineering problem. The Manhattan District had already been formed and it took over at this point. It then induced

E. I. du Pont de Nemours and Company to undertake large-scale manufacture. The du Pont Company accepted the undertaking but stipulated that the work was to be done without profit and without any patent rights going to it. Since du Pont was entering a totally new field—physics rather than chemistry—it was agreed that the Metallurgical Laboratory at Chicago would still do most of the fundamental research and development, while du Pont would contribute its engineering and industrial experience.

Even while the work on experimental piles had been going on, members of the Metallurgical Laboratory had discussed methods for building large industrial plants to produce the amounts of plutonium required for bombs. Preliminary designs had been drawn well before the first self-sustaining pile had been successfully put together. This pile was being run at almost its minimum capacity so that the emitted heat and radioactivity would be small. Under these conditions it would take about 300 years to produce 1 pound of plutonium. Obviously the industrial units would have to step up the rate of production.

It is worth a moment to explain what is involved. Suppose that from a source outside the pile a single slow neutron is supplied to one U-235 atom. It will fission, and produce neutrons. If only one of these emitted neutrons reaches a U-235 atom that fissions and emits neutrons of which only one reaches another U-235 atom and so on, a chain reaction will proceed. The multiplication factor will be 1.00. At any moment there will be just one U-235 atom undergoing fission and the chain will be maintained through this succession of single atoms.

Suppose, however, that we start the series with 100 slow neutrons each causing a U-235 atom to fission. Then the reaction will also just maintain itself, but through 100 chains. The multiplication factor will still be 1.00, but instead of 7 maids with 7 mops, we shall have 700 maids with 700 mops. More plutonium will be produced, more heat liberated, more radioactivity generated. If this is so, then why not 1000 initial atoms, or 1,000,000,000 initial atoms? There is no limit except the heat and radioactivity.

To take care of heat and radioactivity the plants have to be built far from people and from centers of civilization. However, they must be near an extensive power supply so that the plants can have the necessary electricity and the workers in the plants can have homes in which to live. Also the plants should be near a large supply of cold running water for cooling the piles.

The first plant was built at Oak Ridge, in the Tennessee Valley, as the Clinton Engineer Works. The site is remote, but it is near the great power supplies from the TVA. The designs and plans were well along in January 1943, and construction began soon after. Later additions were made, but from the beginning it contained research laboratories as well as production plants. It was a staggering project, as the many photographs show, yet it was much smaller than the final plants at Hanford. The purpose of the Clinton plant was to produce some plutonium and to serve as pilot plant for the chemical separation of plutonium from uranium.

Plutonium is formed from the U-238 in the pile. Means had to be found for chemically removing the plutonium from the other materials. This demanded a knowledge of the chemistry of plutonium, and was also one of the tasks of the Metallurgical Laboratory. In itself this is a fascinating story, because plutonium in microscopic quantities had to be made in one place (first at the University of California, and later at Washington University in St. Louis) and its properties and reactions studied elsewhere. At the end of 1942 about 500-millionths of a gram of plutonium compounds had been produced in pure form. This seems like an absurd amount, but for the microchemists it was ample because they can make experiments with just 1-millionth of a gram.

The scientific information gained in these ways had then to be translated into large-scale production methods, and this was the job of the chemists and engineers at the Clinton separation plant. They accomplished it beautifully, so that their procedures served as the basis for the Hanford plant. In addition, the Clinton laboratories served as a training center for persons later to take over the Hanford plant, for medical studies, for testing, and for innumerable side problems that arose.

2. LARGE-SCALE PRODUCTION OF PLUTONIUM

The final large plutonium plant was built as the Hanford Engineer Works on the west side of the Columbia River in central Washington north of the town of Pasco. Near by was the Grand Coulee Dam, which could supply it with power, and next to it was the Columbia River, part of which could be diverted to run through the piles for cooling purposes.

The construction of the Hanford works was a triumph of modern engineering. Ground was broken on April 6, 1943, for the construction camp. At the height of activity in 1944 there were 60,000 inhabitants of the camp, making it the fourth city of the state. The construction of the first pile— later known as nuclear reactor—was begun on June 7, 1943, and it started to function four months later.

The design of the nuclear reactors for production of plutonium was somewhat different from that of the pile built in Chicago. It is shown in Figure 21. The graphite is now in a practically continuous mass with imbedded pipes through which cool water circulates. The uranium is not in small lumps but in the form of slugs or rods that can be slid in and out of tubular holes.

The uranium rods are sealed in cans for easy handling. This itself was one of the minor headaches at Chicago. For months the precise material to hold the slugs of uranium was under experimental investigation. It had to be some-

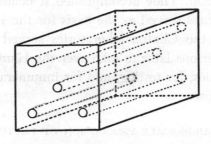

FIGURE 21. THE CONTINUOUS PILE FOR MAKING PLUTONIUM

The graphite is not in bricks, but is packed solid, while the uranium is in the form of rods that are pushed into the tubular holes. The changed U-238 can then be removed and processed for plutonium. Compare the lattice pile in Figure 19.

thing that would not corrode, would not be affected by radiation, would conduct heat easily, and would be available in large quantities. Aluminum turned out to be the best material.

The cooling water was another problem. Obviously the water could not be heated too high because of the animals and plants with which it would come in contact when it returned to the river. Moreover, the water absorbed some of the radioactivity and therefore had to be stored until it became safe again for return to the river.

After some of the uranium in the pile has been converted to plutonium, the rods have to be transferred to a separation plant for the chemical removal of plutonium. One cannot wait until all the uranium has been converted into plutonium because of the accumulation of other products of fission. Just after the first Hanford pile began operating, one of the fission products threatened to "poison" the pile and stop the chain reaction because of its extraordinary capacity for capturing neutrons. Fortunately, enough space was left in the pile so that more uranium slugs could be added to overcome this unexpected difficulty.

Since the fission products are intensely radioactive, thick concrete walls were built between the workers and the chemical vats, and all the processes were accomplished by automatic machinery manipulated by remote control.

In this small volume there is no place to describe details. Many of these details raised problems that engineers face and solve every day whenever they are presented with tasks requiring ingenuity, skill, and technical imagination. Some arose out of the special circumstances of radioactivity, of speed, of lack of pilot-plant experience, and the like. The result was one of the extraordinary enterprises of our time.

3. URANIUM FOR BOMBS IS PRODUCED IN QUANTITY

We have followed the path of plutonium production. In 1943 this seemed the most likely to succeed rapidly. However, the other path, the one through uranium isotope separation, was not neglected. Several different projects were concerned with the segregation of U-235 from its much more prevalent companion U-238. One of the successful large-scale methods was the gaseous diffusion process.

The principle of the diffusion process is quite old. In 1896

Lord Rayleigh had shown that a mixture of two gases of different atomic weight can be partially separated by letting it diffuse through a porous barrier. Aston in 1913 had tried this method for separating neon-20 from neon-22.

In the fall of 1940 John Dunning at Columbia reviewed the prospects of the method and initiated preliminary experiments with funds supplied from one of Urey's contracts with the Navy. By July 1941 an OSRD contract was assigned to Dunning and his associates, and from then on funds were always available for the work. In May 1943 Urey was put in over-all charge and remained so until March 1945, when the laboratory was taken over from Columbia by Carbide and Carbon Chemicals Corporation.

The main point of the diffusion process is that to effect any real separation the gas must diffuse through many barriers. To get 99 per cent U-235 one needs about four thousand stages. One great virtue is that all the stages need not be traversed in order to judge the efficiency; therefore small experimental plants can be set up and tested.

The diffusing gas, uranium hexafluoride, has to be produced, pumps have to be designed and built, barriers have to be invented and tested. The latter involves a nice point. A proper diffusion barrier for the purpose cannot have holes larger than 4 ten-millionths of an inch in diameter. There must be billions of holes and they must not become enlarged or plugged during the diffusion. Naturally one should be able to make the barriers in large numbers and with uniform results. It is wonderful that such barriers were actually developed.

Finally, early in 1943, most of the problems seemed sufficiently near solution so that large-scale plants could be built. In June 1943 the steam power plant that would furnish power for the diffusion plant was begun at Oak Ridge. It is one of the largest power plants of this sort ever built. The other buildings began going up three and four months later. Because of the unit nature of the process, the diffusion plant could be put into production as the sections were built. By the middle of 1944 it was going full strength.

The diffusion process had no dramatic moments such as the Chicago pile, or the Hanford plant. The men worked at the job between 1940 and 1945 with a courage and persistence that are admirable. They solved with wonderful ingenuity and scientific skill problems that seemed almost impossible. I gather that toward the end of 1945 the plant was producing on a sufficiently large scale to make it one of the significant contributors of fissile material.

In the early days of the uranium work, the two most promising separation methods were considered to be the gaseous diffusion process, and the centrifuge process. After 1941 the centrifuge method was studied intensively in two places. The magnitude of the engineering problems proved so great that no large-scale production was ever undertaken, and the method was discontinued.

Only the electromagnetic method of separation was left. The method is J. J. Thomson's old Geissler tubes writ large, and had been used by Aston in his mass spectroscope. It depends on the fact that in a powerful magnetic field a stream of ions will be deviated to a degree depending on the mass of the ions. Figure 20 shows the principle. It will be recalled that with it Nier in 1939 had separated microscopic specks of U-235 from the other uranium isotopes for Dunning and his associates to see which isotope fissions. Nier's apparatus collected a maximum of 1-millionth of a gram of U-235 in a 24-hour day. The question was whether a larger magnet and better conditions could produce more. If so, how many units would be required to produce the necessary pounds of U-235?

The University of California had a piece of apparatus (a cyclotron—of no interest for us, except that it was an arrangement for making a beam of very fast protons) with a large magnet. Under the general direction of E. O. Lawrence the 37-inch magnet was set up for this purpose and by December 1941 it was functioning. In January 1942 it really made fair separations, and by March 1942 it was going so well that Lawrence's hopes seemed to be borne out.

A large research program was initiated in which many physicists were engaged, and this group was strengthened by a British contingent under the leadership of M. L. Oliphant from the University of Birmingham. A larger magnet, with a pole diameter of 184 inches, was put to work and around it were assembled shops and laboratories so that by May 1942 it was ready for use.

In several months of intensive experimentation it became clear that many such units would be required for enough material to be produced to be of military importance. If one unit produces 1/100 gram a day, about 45,000 units would produce 1 pound per day. It was merely a question of cost and time.

Remember that this was in September 1942. No chain reaction had as yet been established and no plutonium production had been initiated. The gaseous diffusion method was promising but not spectacular. Obviously one had to develop the magnetic separation process. Here too the great virtue was that one unit could be built at a time; it was not all or nothing.

The end of 1942 was the time of decision. The self-sustaining chain reaction worked at Chicago. At that time the plutonium plant at Oak Ridge was in the design stage, and the gaseous diffusion plant at Oak Ridge was decided on. At the same time an electromagnetic separation plant was approved for construction at Oak Ridge. These three were located on a tract near the Clinch River.

Construction of the first group of units at Clinton began in March 1943 and by the end of the year it was ready to go. As improvements were made at California they were incorporated in the new units. During the winter of 1944-45 the electromagnetic separation plant was operating full scale and was producing U-235 in sufficient purity for the manufacture of atomic bombs. After the war, cost comparisons indicated that the operation of the gaseous diffusion plant was less expensive than that of the electromagnetic separation plant. The latter was stopped, and finally dismantled, except for the section used to separate stable isotopes of ordinary elements. The gaseous diffusion process, on the other hand, was expanded, and later other plants were built in Paducah, Kentucky, and Portsmouth, Ohio.

4. THE ATOMIC BOMB IS BUILT

We are approaching the end of the wartime story. From three different sources fissile material is being produced in a high degree of purity. There is plutonium-239 from the Hanford plant; there is U-235 from the gaseous diffusion plant at Oak Ridge; and U-235 from the electromagnetic separation plant also at Oak Ridge. We must now use these materials to make an atomic bomb.

A self-sustaining, nuclear chain reaction in a pile such as worked in Chicago and at Hanford has a multiplication factor of 1.00. The fission of each atom of U-235 may release several neutrons, but only one of these reaches another U-235 atom to continue the chain. There may be one such chain or 1,000,000; that depends on the number of U-235 atoms initially set in fission by an outside source. The piles must be constantly watched from behind thick concrete walls to see that the multiplication factor remains at 1.00.

An atomic bomb is something different. Because it is composed of nearly pure plutonium-239 or uranium-235, there is nothing to absorb neutrons except atoms that fission and produce more neutrons. All the neutrons that remain in the lump will result in fission. Assume that from each fissioning atom only 2 neutrons remain in the mass to be absorbed by other atoms. The multiplication factor will be 2.00, and each neutron generation will result in twice the number of splitting atoms that the preceding generation had produced. The first atom that fissions produces 2 effective neutrons. These are absorbed by 2 atoms, which fission and produce 2 neutrons each, making a total of 4 neutrons. Each of these is absorbed by an atom that fissions, with a total result of 8 neutrons available. Thus the generations of splitting atoms number 1, 2, 4, 8, 16, 32, 64, 128, and so on.

Such a reproductive series increases at a fantastic rate. The tenth generation is 1024; the twentieth generation is over a million; the thirtieth generation over a billion; the sixtieth generation is over a billion billion; the ninetieth generation is over a billion billion billion. Suppose each neutron generation lasts 1-millionth of a second. Then in ninety generations or 90-millionths of a second, over a billion billion billion atoms will have fissioned. In the minutest fraction of a second, the whole mass of material will have fissioned and released the energies that we know about. If an explosion is defined as the sudden release of a large amount of energy in a small space, then this is an explosion.

The important point is the critical mass. If a piece of uranium-235 or plutonium-239 is smaller than the critical mass, not enough neutrons will remain inside for the multiplication factor to reach 1.00, and when fission is initiated it will die out. If a piece is larger than the critical mass, then even if its multiplication factor is only slightly greater than 1.00 it will explode almost instantaneously after the first atom fissions because each atomic fission lasts less than a millionth of a second. Actually there are many stray neutrons around from cosmic rays, so that the mere accumulation of fissile material beyond the critical mass will instantly result in an explosion when one of these stray neutrons gets into the mass. Most of the technical troubles in producing the bomb actually came from the amazingly short time between the arrival of the first neutron and the explosion.

Essentially then, the construction of an atomic bomb is merely an arrangement for rapidly assembling a piece of pure Pu-239 or U-235 larger than the critical mass, and supplying it with a few neutrons. Imagine a mass of U-235 or of Pu-239 just smaller than the critical size. This will not explode even if we supply it with a few neutrons. Then imagine that we have a smaller piece of the same material at some distance. It too will not explode. But if it were added to the larger piece, the two would form a mass well above the critical size. Therefore just imagine a machine that can bring these two pieces together with great rapidity, and you have an atomic bomb. For instance, the smaller mass may be in the form of a bullet that can be shot from a distance of a few feet into a prepared hole in the larger mass, which is receiving a few neutrons. Almost at once after the bullet hits there will be an explosion.

What is the critical size? The earliest estimates back in 1939 had been between 2 and 200 pounds. These estimates were based on the available measurements of the distance that a neutron can go before it is captured, and on the distance that a neutron needs to be from a uranium nucleus in order to be captured by it—a factor called the "capture cross section" of the uranium nucleus. These were rough measurements and obviously needed careful going over. They would be needed the moment U-235 and Pu-239 became available, even for so simple a decision as how to store the material, in what sizes, and how far apart.

There were hundreds of such questions that needed investigation. How much energy will a bomb produce? Where should it be exploded, high in the air, under water, or on the ground? What will happen to the radioactive gases produced? Can one make a bomb smaller than the critical size provided neutron reflectors are placed around it? What are good neutron reflectors or tampers? Will the bomb fly apart before the chain reaction has finished, or can it be held together until all the atoms have fissioned? These questions could not wait until the last minute when Pu-239 or U-235 had become available. Nor, worse luck, could one try small bombs to see how they would work. With an atomic bomb it is all or nothing. The problem is thus one of combining the most accurate measurements with the best computation from theory.

Some of these matters were already under discussion in 1941. Early in 1942 Gregory Breit of the University of Wisconsin had initiated a number of experimental and theoretical studies at various institutions concerned with precisely such questions. Later that summer J. R. Oppenheimer of the University of California formed a group there for further theoretical studies and became the co-ordinator of all the experimental work. By the end of the summer of 1942 it seemed essential to set up a separate laboratory just for these purposes.

For secrecy and safety it was located on an isolated and deserted mesa thirty miles from Santa Fe, at Los Alamos, New Mexico. Oppenheimer became the director and arrived in March 1943. He assembled around him a great concentration of theoretical and experimental physicists and in an amazingly short time built what has since become probably the best equipped physics research laboratory in the world. He was joined by such familiar people as Hans Bethe, Enrico Fermi, Niels Bohr of Denmark, James Chadwick from Cambridge, England, who brought with him a whole British contingent, and dozens and dozens of other scientists, all of whom worked in this Shangri-La.

There was a Theoretical Physics Division, an Experimental Nuclear Physics Division, a Chemistry and Metallurgy Division, an Ordnance Division, an Explosives Division, a Bomb Physics Division, and an Advanced Development Division, each under a well-known director. Much of what they all did is still buried in secrecy. This, however, is known. As the result of their labors they constructed atomic bombs that worked.

5. THE SECRET IS OUT

No theory is acceptable until it has been put to the test of experiment. The theory that underlies the atomic bomb is an elaborate structure that has grown from simple beginnings. We started with salt dissolving in water, which yielded the concept of atoms. Since then we have enlarged and complicated this basic atom until its architecture is a mass of whirling electrons in shell after shell around a nucleus that has its own inner complexities of neutrons, protons, and charges tied in knots by binding energies.

Sometime in the course of the story the reader has probably said to himself that this theoretical piling of Pelion on Olympus and of Ossa on Pelion is too much. First we measure the combining ratios of substances. They turn out to be almost whole numbers, and we have an explanation. Then because they are not really whole numbers we devise a theory to explain the differences: we invent isotopes. But even in terms of the new theory there still are differences from whole numbers, so we invent packing factors. Then we invent fast neutrons and slow neutrons and nuclear fission and capture cross section. Finally we predict a theoretical atomic bomb, which cannot be demonstrated on a small scale. And we expect the world to supply hundreds of millions of dollars to build factories employing thousands of people to produce a few pounds of something that we insist must be kept in small packages.

It seems fantastic. It *is* fantastic. To the scientist who works daily in the laboratory in terms of a theory, it becomes a familiar reality. He watches it grow. He predicts a piece here or there, and either he or a colleague elsewhere tests it and finds it true or false. The whole structure gradually assumes a kind of certainty that to the outsider who has not followed its development, seems wholly visionary and a little mad.

The atomic bomb project was infinitely more complex than the usual scientific experiment. Ordinarily, the step from prediction to practice is not large or long delayed, and in the course of the development, progress can be established by small-scale experiments. With the atomic bomb the realization of theoretical prediction involved thousands of people, vast amounts of money, factories, towns, secrets, the Army, the Navy, and the highest echelons of government and science. And nothing to show for it until the final single all-or-nothing test.

Let no one imagine that the scientists and military men who assembled at Alamogordo in the earliest morning hours of July 16, 1945, were not fully conscious of these implications. More than this. The scientists knew that they were about to open a new age in human history. They had all wrestled with the problem during the war years. Many had even made official representations against the use of the bomb on civilian populations. Not only were the military and industrial implications evident to them, but they had envisaged the social and political repercussions to come. Here they were, making the experiment toward which all this effort had been directed (see Chapter XI).

True to the canons of drama, there was a final suspense. The whole mechanism had been machined with the utmost precision and was being assembled. For a few anguished moments, one part became wedged tightly and would not budge. Robert F. Bacher, originally of Cornell, who actually manipulated the assembly, remained coolest of all and succeeded in putting the parts together. From then on everything went according to schedule. The explosion took place, and emitted the light, heat, sound, radioactivity, and blast with which the world has since become familiar. The secret was out for all the world to see. An atomic bomb was possible.

This is the real point. We have all heard about the secrets

of the atomic bomb, how they were guarded, and how important it is to keep or not to keep them to ourselves. Spies have been busy—and apparently quite successful—in penetrating the walls of secrecy. The reader knows now that there are no *fundamental* secrets. Atomic energy was known and evaluated in 1900; the basic equation was written in 1905. Its meaning in terms of atomic structure has come slowly with each new discovery about the nature of matter and energy. If there was one great secret, we gave it away in July 1945. It was that a chain reaction *is* possible and that it can be used to make a bomb. That was the meaning of the explosion at Alamogordo.

We have learned since that the development leading to this explosion was known to a foreign power—the Soviet Union, from which, as much as from Germany, we wanted to keep it secret—through the activity of that power's agents. One of these, the German-born physicist Klaus Fuchs, was a member of the inner circle at Los Alamos. This means that Alamogordo and Hiroshima came as no surprise to the Soviet rulers. They knew of the extent of the effort we put into developing atomic explosives, and of the approaching success. Without this knowledge they could conceivably have considered atomic energy too remote a topic to concern their scientists and engineers when half of their country was overrun by the enemy. Very likely the reports of their agents caused the Soviet rulers to start their own atomic development in 1943. The same reports could have told them which ways of approach proved promising in America, and which were beset with pitfalls, and thus saved them months of their own orientation experiments. In brief, spies may have accelerated the acquisition of atomic weapons by the Soviet Union by perhaps as much as two or three years.

However, it remains a delusion to think—as many do—that the only way for the Soviet Union to make an atomic bomb within a few years after Hiroshima was to "steal our secret." If we could think of several ways of doing each step from uranium fission to atomic bomb, so can another group of scientists. In fact, the British were ahead of us in 1941, and they might possibly have given us a good run if Britain had not been so near Germany that its plants and cities were steadily bombed. We were far away from the scene of the war, and the British sent their best people to work with us. So did the Canadians. Even Niels Bohr from Denmark came here to help. Moreover, we had on our side some of the best brains in the refugees from Germany, Austria, Hungary, and Italy.

All these men and women worked against time and were always haunted by the possibility that the Germans might get there first, or that a chain reaction could not be established. Some of them hoped it could never be established. The social and political crises that lay ahead were all too clear, and some of them hoped even against hope that some quirk of nature would make it impossible to have a chain reaction. It might have turned up at any stage in the process and made further progress impossible. That uncertainty is gone. Alamogordo made it plain that a chain reaction with uranium and plutonium can work.

Of course there have been—and still are—many technical and engineering secrets. They do not involve anything fundamental, but instead they are the kind that competing motor-car manufacturers keep from one another. In a short time competent engineers and inventors can duplicate them and probably improve them. This fact does not belittle the ingenuity, imagination, and skill involved in technical and engineering work. But we Americans have no monopoly of such ingenuity, imagination, and skill.

The design of the actual bomb itself can be considered like the design of any other piece of ordnance. We keep designs of our submarines secret, also of our torpedoes, guns, bombsights, of practically every important piece of ordnance. Other countries do likewise. We tried to do so with the designs of the Hiroshima and Nagasaki bombs but did not succeed. We are undoubtedly trying to do it with the designs of our more recent weapons, and for these our efforts may be more successful. This is not unimportant, but the significance of successful concealment of our atomic devices was vastly exaggerated in the public mind. The shock of the supposed loss of these secrets by espionage activities of the British physicist Alan Nunn May, of Fuchs, and of the Rosenberg-Greenglass group in America, caused public consternation. The two Rosenbergs were executed as having "endangered the whole future of America," and the scare contributed largely to the excesses of the "McCarthy era." And yet, there is—there never has been—any *basic* secret of the atom bomb.

IX

ATOMIC BOMBS
BECOME PLENTIFUL AND VARIED

1. THE ATOMIC ENERGY COMMISSION TAKES OVER

When atomic bombs were dropped on Hiroshima and Nagasaki, they were the only two in existence, but already the
two were different. The bomb dropped on Hiroshima was
loaded with U-235, and exploded by firing one piece of this
material, like a bullet, into another one, like a target; the
two pieces added together to a larger-than-critical mass.
This mechanism was so simple that it was not even tried
out before use; in the test explosion at Alamogordo a few
weeks earlier another, more ingenious mechanism had been
tried out, and this was the one used in the Nagasaki bomb.
Its principle (revealed during the atomic spy trial) was
called "implosion": a sphere of plutonium was surrounded
by a number of high-explosive charges, "shaped" so as to
direct the main force of their explosion inward; the resulting
compression caused the fissionable mass to become "super-
critical." The Nagasaki bomb was so much more efficient
(that is, the fraction of the fissionable material which really
fissioned instead of being scattered by the explosion was so
much higher) that its effect was about the same as that of
the Hiroshima bomb, despite a much smaller fissionable
load.

After these two shots ended the war in the Far East, the production and development of atomic weapons in America went into a slump. Most of the scientific personnel left the Manhattan District laboratories for academic positions. The uncertainty about the future organization of the project, the reluctance of scientists to work on secret weapon research except in the face of emergency, and the hope that negotiations for international control of atomic energy and abolition of atomic weapons would soon be successful, combined to bring the work at the atomic-energy laboratories almost to a standstill in 1946.

An intense controversy raged during this period over the future direction of atomic-energy work in America. Two bills were introduced into Congress. The first one would have made possible the continuation of military control of the project; the other, offered by Senator Brien McMahon, proposed an essentially civilian rule. Largely through the efforts of scientists and of public-opinion groups mobilized by them, the McMahon bill became law on August 1, 1946. It established a complete government monopoly of the production and ownership of fissionable materials and put the development of atomic energy in America, for military and non-military purposes, into the hands of a commission (the Atomic Energy Commission, AEC) appointed directly by the President and consisting of five full-time members, all civilians, with a general manager, a part-time General Advisory Committee, and several other statutory advisory bodies. A Joint Congressional Committee on Atomic Energy was established by the same law, to "keep watch" over the Commission. David E. Lilienthal, chairman of the Tennessee Valley Authority, became the first chairman of the Atomic Energy Commission; J. R. Oppenheimer, the wartime head of the Los Alamos laboratory, the first chairman of the General Advisory Committee; and Senator Brien McMahon, the author of the Atomic Energy Act, the first chairman of the Joint Congressional Committee on Atomic Energy.

When the AEC took over from the Manhattan District administration on January 1, 1947, the international atomic-energy control negotiations had already shown a tendency to drag out, and relations between the United States and the Soviet Union a tendency to deteriorate badly, so that restoration of the activity of the Los Alamos weapons laboratory appeared an urgent task. Dr. Robert Bacher, the one scientist among the first five commissioners, described later his dismay at the "empty larder" he found when he first went to inspect the Los Alamos "atomic arsenal."

2. PLUTONIUM AND U-235 BECOME CHEAP AND PLENTIFUL

The enthusiasm with which Mr. Lilienthal and his colleagues began their work sprang above all from their hope to make atomic energy a new source of abundant life for America and the world, but their legislative mandate, and the darkening world horizon, called for first attention to be given to the acceleration of atomic weapon production. The commission discharged this mandate with great success. The Los Alamos laboratory again became one of the best-equipped and best-staffed physical laboratories in the world. The plutonium-producing atomic furnaces at Hanford, threatened with extinction because of radiation damage, were repaired and restored to full production; to increase the rate of plutonium production, new reactors were added to the three original ones. A simpler, more effective method of chemical separation of plutonium was put into operation. The construction of a new plutonium-producing plant, dwarfing Hanford, was undertaken at Savannah, Georgia. (Another function of this plant is to produce tritium—"super-heavy" hydrogen—for "thermonuclear" weapons, of which more later.)

The electromagnetic separation plant at Oak Ridge was closed down, because it had proved less economical in operation than the gaseous diffusion plant. The latter was considerably enlarged and two new gaseous diffusion plants were built, at Paducah, Kentucky, and Portsmouth, Ohio, respectively.

By these developments, which meant additional investment of billions of public money, the supply of the two fissionable nuclear explosives—plutonium and uranium-235—was increased severalfold above the rate reached in 1946; while their unit price was considerably reduced. It can now be said that atomic destructive power is by far the cheapest; a dollar spent on atomic weapons buys much more destruction than does a dollar invested in the production of ordinary explosives.

3. LARGER AND SMALLER ATOMIC BOMBS ARE BUILT

As the supply of nuclear explosives grew, the Los Alamos laboratory busied itself with the invention of a variety of atomic weapons. The first bombs, transported to Hiroshima and Nagasaki in specially enlarged bomb bays of giant B-36 bombers, were heavy and unwieldy. It proved possible to reduce the size of the machinery surrounding the small explosive core until the bomb could be lifted by a fighter bomber, capable of rising from a short landing strip or from the deck of an aircraft carrier; finally, the bomb was even fitted into an artillery shell and fired from a mobile Army rifle. True, this extreme reduction in bulk could be achieved only by sacrificing the efficiency of the explosion, thus wasting most of the fissionable material, but even the small fraction that actually exploded produced an effect never yet achieved by an artillery shell.

The reduction in the size of the bomb, and the plentiful supply of nuclear explosives, converted atomic bombs from rarity weapons, to be used only against a few large "strategic" targets, such as big industrial cities, into mass weapons which could be used, in a future war, by the hundred, if not by the thousand, even against relatively small "tactical" targets, such as troops massed for attack, bridgeheads, or enemy supply dumps.

This development of "tactical" atomic bombs has been rather widely misinterpreted as meaning that atomic bombs with fissionable loads much smaller than those used in Japan could now be fabricated; so that a proportionally larger number of bombs could be made from the same amount of explosives. The requirement of critical size however cannot be avoided; consequently, a tactical atomic bomb is not a bomb containing only a minute amount of fissionable material, but a bomb that carries a full fissionable load but has a housing and detonating device small and light enough to permit its use under field conditions, scattering most of the load into the wind.

Parallel with the development of the "tactical" atomic bombs, increasingly powerful "strategic" bombs have been developed, until President Eisenhower could report, in December 1953, that fission bombs twenty-five times more powerful than the Hiroshima bomb—in other words, equivalent to perhaps 400,000 tons of TNT—have been made and tested.

The increasing cheapness, abundance, and variety of

atomic weapons caused Senator Brien McMahon to suggest, as early as 1951, that the main emphasis of the American armament effort should be put on atomic arms, to obtain the greatest military power at the lowest cost. American military planners gradually became accustomed to this idea, until, in 1954, reliance on "massive retaliation" (that is, primarily on atomic weapons) became the official strategic doctrine of the United States.

A bomb twenty-five times more powerful than the one that had obliterated Hiroshima with about 100,000 casualties is dreadful enough to contemplate, but even this bomb fades out before a new and much more powerful engine of destruction—the ultimate result of application of nuclear physics to war—the so-called "thermonuclear" or "hydrogen" bomb. This development, however, requires a separate chapter, since it is based on nuclear phenomena different from those we have considered previously.

4. OTHER COUNTRIES ACQUIRE ATOMIC BOMBS

When the existence of atomic bombs was revealed to the world by the bombing of Hiroshima and Nagasaki and the publication of the Smyth Report, much guessing went on about the time it might take other nations, and the Soviet Union in particular, to acquire similar weapons. Some military and political leaders said ten or twenty years, but scientists were much less optimistic. The most carefully weighed estimate[1] was made by two physicists, Hans Bethe and Frederick Seitz. They concluded that about five years was the most probable length of time Soviet scientists would need to develop their own atomic bombs, assuming

[1] In the collection *One World or None* (New York: Whittlesey House, 1946).

they had access only to the generally available information. It was close to four years after the bombing of Hiroshima when the first atomic explosion actually went off in Russia; President Truman announced the fact on September 23, 1949. The difference between the two figures may be an approximate measure of the acceleration of the Soviet program brought about by the access of Soviet agents to the secrets of the wartime American project. Also, these reports could have stimulated a concentrated attack on the problem of thermonuclear weapons, thus explaining why the first Soviet thermonuclear explosion occurred less than a year after the Americans' first one. In fact, Soviet spokesmen claimed that theirs was the first test of a true hydrogen bomb, as contrasted to the earthbound, massive device used in the earlier American test.

In the next decade, from 1953 to 1963, significant atomic-weapon developments were mostly in thermonuclear "fusion" bombs, discussed in the next chapter. The original "fission" bombs were relegated to the role of "tactical" battlefield weapons, while the much more powerful fusion bombs took over as "city-busting" weapons—though a "small" fission bomb proved capable of wiping out a city of 200,000 inhabitants!

The considerably larger number of American low-level tests, compared to that of corresponding Soviet tests, suggests that the United States has stayed ahead of the Soviet Union in the variety and sophistication—and probably also in the number—of atomic weapons. Both sides in the Soviet-American arms race have accumulated an arsenal of thermonuclear weapons sufficient to destroy each other many times over. Under these conditions, relative numbers do not have much significance.

The question of how we know about Soviet bomb tests should be mentioned here, since, in contrast to the United States, the Soviet leaders have told the world about their tests only on occasions when this appeared useful for propaganda purposes. But even a "small" nuclear-weapon test creates such chemical and physical disturbances that it can be detected far from the site of the explosion. The first Soviet tests were identified by American monitors because of the radioactivity they created in the upper atmosphere.

Subsequently other highly sensitive methods of detection were developed, of which seismography (mechanical detection of earth motions) has received the most attention, because it alone permits detection, halfway around the globe, of underground nuclear explosions, the radioactive products of which remain confined in the cavern. By 1964, the only tests which a nation could hope to keep secret were underground explosions with energies of a few kilotons of TNT equivalent, far below the "Hiroshima standard." Since even such small tests could be useful in weapons development, no agreement has yet been reached between the United States and the Soviet Union on an all-inclusive test ban. In 1963, however, an agreement on the prohibition of all but underground testing of nuclear weapons was reached by the United States, the USSR, and Great Britain, joined by most other nations, with the notable exception of France and the Chinese People's Republic, both of which openly aim at developing their own nuclear weapons, and do not want to renounce atmospheric tests.

Of course, a nation wants not only to have bombs but also be able to deliver them. In this field too, the Soviet Union, long behind America, has made rapid progress. This problem assumed an entirely new aspect with the development of long-range rockets, which can carry thermonuclear warheads more than 7000 miles. These "intercontinental ballistic missiles" (ICBMs) have become the main direct threats of the Soviet Union to America and vice versa. Hundreds of ICBMs are poised on both sides, ready to strike around half the world on short notice. Since many ICBMs are in underground "silos" invulnerable to any but a direct hit by a megaton bomb, each side has a retaliatory capacity which cannot be eliminated by surprise attack.

In addition to this "invulnerable nuclear deterrent," nuclear missiles are carried by atomic-propelled submarines, which can lurk practically indefinitely underwater near target areas. Furthermore, many launchers for short-range nuclear missiles are installed in Europe, particularly on the Soviet side, threatening instantaneous destruction of Western Europe. A Soviet attempt to put the United States in similar jeopardy by installing short-range missiles in Cuba failed in 1962 because of the American threat of military intervention.

After World War II, the countries of Western Europe hoped that an international control system would soon stop atomic-arms production in the United States and Russia. As this hope receded, Great Britain began to produce enough plutonium to make atomic bombs. Hanford-type plutonium-production reactors were constructed at Sellafield, Cumberland, and soon atomic bombs were tested—the first on October 1, 1952, at Montebello Island, off the northwest coast of Australia. By 1964 Great Britain had its own sizable nuclear-weapon arsenal, but it was still much smaller than those of the United States or the USSR. One major British political party argues that such a token nuclear force does not justify its costs, and proposes to abandon it and rely on American nuclear power, provided that Great Britain can obtain a voice in any decision to use this power in Europe.

The French first restricted their atomic-energy projects to research, but recently they built plutonium-production reactors and developed atomic bombs. With her first test explosion in the Sahara, France joined the "nuclear club" as a very junior but enthusiastic member. President Charles de Gaulle considers the French nuclear force, however small, as the prerequisite of true political sovereignty.

It seems safe to assert that, barring an effective agreement on atomic disarmament, the two major world powers will retain enough atomic and hydrogen weapons to inflict wholesale destruction, while several other countries will own at least token atomic-bomb arsenals. Peace will have to be maintained by mutual fear of these armaments. The only alternative seems to be to end the existence of sovereign nations capable of arming themselves as they please and using these arms when they so desire, and to establish a world-wide authority to enforce disarmament of all nations to a safe level.

Some may say that a third alternative exists—that all nations, while retaining their sovereignty, may acquire enough wisdom to discard atomic armaments by voluntary agreement and live side by side in peace forever after, as the United States and Canada live now. Whether this solution is more likely than the creation of a world authority of law is uncertain, since it presumes that no single nation will ever permit fanatics of any persuasion to get hold of the government and use its available technological capacities to fulfill dreams of personal power, or to impose by force on others their own ideas of world salvation.

X

"SUPERBOMBS" ARE BUILT

The new type of atomic bomb, which we shall now discuss, was first referred to in hushed conversations between Manhattan Project scientists as the "superbomb." The correct scientific designation is "thermonuclear"; but these bombs have also been called "fusion" bombs, because they are based on reactions in which two small nuclei are "fused" together, instead of one large nucleus being broken in two, as in fission. Since hydrogen—in its rare isotopic forms—is the main explosive ingredient of such bombs, they are also popularly known as "hydrogen bombs" or, abbreviated, "H-bombs," as contrasted to the original "fission bombs" or "A-bombs."

Let us consider the physical foundations of this ultimate destructive application of nuclear physics.

Figure 15, looked at upside down—which is the best way to look at it—represents a cross section of a valley, with a steep right bank and a more gently sloping left bank. The stable arrangement of protons and neutrons is represented by the bottom of this valley—elements in the neighborhood of iron. The nuclei of the heavy elements, such as uranium, and those of the light elements—particularly hydrogen, the lightest one—represent relatively unstable structures, higher up the two banks. They could be made to yield energy by being transformed into nuclei of medium weight, as water running into the bottom of the valley from one of its banks can be made to turn a wheel.

So far, we have dealt only with the crumbling of the left bank, the fission of uranium (or thorium) into barium, krypton, and other middle-weight elements. This "heavy-weight" end of the natural system of chemical elements was the first to offer the possibility of large-scale release of nuclear energy, because dislodging a single stone on this bank can produce an avalanche, so that the work used to set the first stone into motion is regained a millionfold in the energy acquired by the avalanche as it reaches the bottom.

No such luck—or rather, disaster—is possible on the "light-weight" end of the periodic system. This does not mean that explosive nuclear reactions are altogether impossible with light elements—only that such reactions cannot be initiated as easily as the explosive fission of plutonium or of uranium-235. A single neutron introduced into a chunk of fissionable material can set off its explosion, but the explosive fusion of light elements can be initiated only by heating them to an extremely high temperature.

All chain reactions have in common the fact that the transformation of one particle—nucleus, atom, or molecule—causes others to follow suit. There are, however, two possible mechanisms of this involvement, which can be described as "particle chains" and "thermal chains." In the first case, the reaction is initiated by a particle and in turn produces particles that can carry the reaction on. In the second case, the reaction is initiated by local heating and in turn produces enough heat to spread itself.

Explosive fission and explosive fusion are examples of these two types of chain reaction in nuclear chemistry. Both have analogies in ordinary chemistry, and it may be useful to consider these less violent and more familiar examples, as an introduction to understanding the difference between the atomic bomb and the thermonuclear bomb.

Thermal chain reactions are the common mechanism of most chemical explosions—whether of dynamite, trinitrotoluene, or gasoline vapor in an internal combustion engine. Particle chains, on the other hand, are relatively rare in chemistry; a good example is the reaction of a mixture of chlorine and hydrogen gas, initiated by a beam of light. The light quantum is absorbed by a molecule of chlorine (which is a green gas), and causes it to break into two chlorine atoms:

$$(1) \qquad Cl_2 + light \rightarrow Cl + Cl$$

Chlorine atoms react with hydrogen molecules:

$$(2) \qquad Cl + H_2 \rightarrow HCl + H + 0.05 \text{ electron-volt}$$

forming hydrogen chloride, HCl, and a hydrogen atom, H, which in turn reacts with a chlorine molecule:

$$(3) \qquad H + Cl_2 \rightarrow HCl + Cl + 1.93 \text{ electron-volt}$$

giving hydrogen chloride and a chlorine atom and releasing slightly under 2 electron-volts of energy—and so on, until all chlorine or all hydrogen (whichever is present in smaller quantity) is consumed. The similarity of this chemical chain reaction to the nuclear chain reaction of fission is obvious; the light quantum plays the same role as the neutron that initiates fission, and the atoms H and Cl the same role as the "fission neutrons" that carry the reaction on.[1] In contrast

[1] It will be noted that in both cases, the chain is carried on by *neutral* particles—atoms H or Cl, or neutrons. In fusion reactions, where neutrons cannot serve as reaction carriers, *positively charged* nuclei must react directly; since they repulse each other strongly, they cannot be brought together close enough for reaction unless they have been first accelerated to

to the fission reaction in the bomb, the chemical chain reaction, described by equations (1), (2), and (3), remains "linear" and does not "branch"; in other words, it proceeds steadily, but does not grow with time like an avalanche. This is because each step produces only *one* particle able to carry forward the reaction—not two or three such particles, as in fission, where the next step can be two or three times faster than the preceding one. (In an atomic reactor, the fission process is artificially slowed down by neutron-absorbing control rods, so that the chains remain linear.)

However, the hydrogen-chlorine reaction, initiated by a beam of light, may—and often does—end in an explosion. This happens if the size and shape of the reaction vessel, and the pressure of gases in it, are such that the reaction *heat* produced in step (3) cannot be conducted away rapidly enough. The gas will then heat up as the chain proceeds until the direct reaction between chlorine and hydrogen molecules:

(4) $H_2 + Cl_2 \rightarrow 2\ HCl + 1.88$ electron-volts

becomes possible. The heat supplied by this reaction will cause the temperature of the gas mass to rise still farther, thus, in turn, accelerating the reactions (2), (3), and (4), and so on. The linear particle chain thus culminates in a thermal explosion.

A thermal explosion does not need to be initiated by a particle chain, as in the preceding example. Usually, thermal explosions are brought under way by local heating—a flame, a spark, or an auxiliary heat-producing chemical reaction,

---

enormous velocities, enabling them to overcome the repulsion. This explains why reactions between light nuclei need high thermal activation. Fusable nuclei do not fall into each other spontaneously but have to be pushed violently toward each other before they fuse.

such as the decomposition of mercury fulminate in the per-
cussion cap of a cartridge. (This compound is so unstable
that it will decompose by mechanical shock, produced, for
example, by releasing the trigger in a gun.)

That thermal explosions should be possible also in nuclear
physics, particularly among the unstable light elements, was
suggested as soon as the packing-factor curve (Figure 15)
was first traced; but before the advent of the fission bomb,
artificial production of "thermonuclear explosions" appeared
out of the question. To explain why, we must return to
chemistry and dwell a little more on the concept of activation energy.

We live in an unstable world. Our own bodies, wood,
coal—all organic matter on earth—are "combustible"; in other
words, they are capable of burning if provided with oxygen
and with some agent (fire, electricity) which will help the
reaction to get under way. Respiration in the body, and
rotting of organic matter, are slow combustions, made possible by the catalytic action of certain compounds, called
enzymes, present in animal bodies, or secreted by bacteria.

Combustion of organic matter releases energy—as well we
know when we use fuel to heat our houses—but to *initiate*
this energy release, some energy must be first supplied from
the outside, such as the heat of a match. This chemical activation is similar to the mechanical effort needed to dislodge
a stone lying near the top of a hill, imbedded in earth; once
lifted out of the ground and pushed over the bank, the stone
will start rolling down, gathering speed. A scientist would
say that the stone, before it was dislodged (or organic matter, before it was ignited) was in a "potential minimum," or
"potential hole" and had to be pushed over a "potential barrier," to send it on its way toward stable mechanical (or chem-

ical) equilibrium. The potential barrier can be due to gravitation, as in the case of the stone, or to electrical forces, as in the case of chemical systems, in which attraction between atoms and molecules—or their constituent electrons and nuclei—must be overcome to start a reaction. The energy used to overcome the barrier is called activation energy and is usually supplied by "heating"; that is, by setting atoms and molecules in violent, disorderly agitation, causing them to collide with greater energy, or to vibrate violently. When two automobiles collide at 10 miles per hour, the force of the impact is just enough to dent the fenders; when they collide at 50 miles per hour, the steel bodies are crumpled and heavily bolted parts are dislodged. The same difference exists between the encounters of molecules at low and at elevated temperatures. A rule of thumb applicable to many chemical reactions is that heating by 10 degrees centigrade doubles their speed. In other words, the speed of a chemical reaction rises with temperature in a geometrical progression; or, as the chemist might say, exponentially. A reaction that requires for its completion 10 years at room temperature (20 degrees centigrade) may be completed in 14 days at 100 degrees, in 20 minutes at 200 degrees, and in only slightly more than a second at 300 degrees.

At any given temperature, the average energy of the molecules is proportional to temperature; however, it is not distributed among all the particles uniformly, but according to a certain statistical distribution law, which says that, at any given moment, a few molecules have much less energy and a few molecules much more than the average. It is the exceptionally fast particles that initiate reactions. The higher the temperature, the higher the proportion of such fast particles and the faster the reaction. The average thermal energy at 300 degrees centigrade is about 0.06 electron-volt; nevertheless, a reaction with an activation energy of 1 electron-volt may get under way at that temperature because a small but sufficient number of "extra-fast" molecules have fifteen times the average energy at that temperature.

Exactly the same is true of thermonuclear reactions—with the important difference that the activation energies needed to initiate them are millions of times larger than those required to start chemical reactions, and that they therefore become possible only at temperatures of millions of degrees. No wonder; the particles (neutrons and protons) are packed in a nucleus so much more tightly than the "valence electrons" responsible for chemical activity are packed in atoms that an enormously greater violence of collision is needed to dislodge them. In other words, the potential holes are much deeper in nuclear than in ordinary chemistry.

Atom-smashing machines (such as cyclotrons, or betatrons) permit us to expose various nuclei to bombardment with atomic projectiles. This fire is too scattered to start a self-sustaining, explosive nuclear reaction in the target, but the technique of making the tracks of single nuclei visible provides a means of finding out what minimum energy the projectile must have to shatter a certain nucleus. In this way, it is possible to estimate the thermal activation energies that will be needed to initiate different nuclear reactions, and thus to predict the temperatures at which these reactions will get under way.

Estimates of nuclear activation energy were first used to interpret the source of solar energy. It has been known for a long time that the sun and other stars are continuously losing immense amounts of energy by sending radiations into space. These losses can be estimated—in the case of the sun, we have only to multiply the amount of solar energy received by the earth by the ratio of the surface of a sphere with the diameter of the earth's orbit to the cross section of the earth. Knowing the mass of the sun, we can then figure out at what rate the sun would be cooling down if the only source of its radiation were its heat; we find that, however high the temperature might have been at the time the earth was created, the sun would have long since become a cold, dead body, like a poker taken out of a furnace, if its heat were not constantly being replenished from some hidden source. This source is provided by thermonuclear reactions, made possible by the extremely high temperature (estimated at 20 million degrees) in the interior of the sun. Physicists have discovered several nuclear reactions which could proceed sufficiently rapidly at that temperature to contribute to keeping the sun hot. The best known of these is "Bethe's carbon cycle," named after Hans Bethe, who first suggested it. The net result of this cycle is the combination of four hydrogen nuclei, $_1H^1$, into one helium nucleus, $_2H^4$:

$$(5) \qquad 4\,_1H^1 \rightarrow\, _2He^4 + 2\,_1e^0 + 26 \text{ million electron-volts}$$

The emission of two positrons, $_1e^0$ (see page 96), is necessary to conserve the four elementary electric charges of the four hydrogen nuclei. The energy released in this reaction (26 million electron-volts) can be compared with the 220 million electron-volts liberated in the fission of a uranium atom, and with the less than 2 electron-volts freed by the hydrogen-chlorine explosion already described.

In chemistry we are familiar with the fact that many reactions can occur only with the help of "catalysts"—chemical marriage brokers, who cause compounds to react without being themselves changed by the reaction. Very often the mechanism of catalyzed chemical reactions consists of several consecutive steps, with the catalyst entering one of them but re-emerging in another one. The function of catalysts is to open new reaction paths, which may be roundabout but are not obstructed by high potential barriers, and therefore require a minimum of activation energy. A catalyzed reaction is like a sequence of passes in a football game which fool the defense and end in a touchdown.

The same principle applies to nuclear chemistry. In the Bethe cycle, carbon nuclei serve as "nuclear catalysts." The cycle goes through the sequence of reactions shown in Table I:

TABLE I

		TIME CONSTANT*
(6)	$_1H^1 + {_6}C^{12} \rightarrow {_7}N^{13}$	40,000 yr
(7)	$_7N^{13} \rightarrow {_6}C^{13} + {_1}e^0$	10 min
(8)	$_6C^{13} + {_1}H^1 \rightarrow {_7}N^{14}$	7000 yr
(9)	$_7N^{14} + {_1}H^1 \rightarrow {_8}O^{15}$	1 million yr
(10)	$_8O^{15} \rightarrow {_7}N^{15} + {_1}e^0$	2 min
(11)	$_7N^{15} + {_1}H^1 \rightarrow {_6}C^{12} + {_2}He^4$	20 yr
(12) net result	$4 {_1}H^1 \rightarrow {_2}He^4 + 2 {_1}e^0$	

* The time constant figures in this column are for conditions of temperature, density, and concentration of the reacting elements such as exist at the center of the sun; that is, 20,000,000 degrees centigrade, 100 times the density of water, and about 1/3 hydrogen by weight.

To obtain equation (12), equations (6) to (11) have been added algebraically, thus eliminating nuclei which are regenerated later in the cycle. The right-hand column contains the rate constants of all reaction steps—which means, roughly, the times needed for their half-completion. In the case of steps requiring collisions of two nuclei, such as (6), (8), (9), and (11), the time constants are calculated for a hydrogen concentration of 1/3. Obviously reaction (9) is the bottle-neck which determines the duration of the whole cycle; because of this bottleneck, each carbon nucleus in the sun can mediate a hydrogen-to-helium conversion once in several million years. The over-all rate of hydrogen "condensation" to helium in the sun, via the Bethe cycle, is slowed down by the combination of the long time during which a carbon nucleus is "tied up" in each cycle and the relative scarcity of these nuclei in the sun. Similarly, the limited amount of the thyroid-gland hormone present in the human body, and the relatively low body temperature, keep the rate of our respiration steady and low.

The Bethe cycle is not the only mechanism of "burning" hydrogen nuclei that can contribute to the energy of the sun. The reaction sequence in Table II may be equally, if not more, important:

TABLE II

		TIME CONSTANT*
(13)	$_1H^1 + _1H^1 \rightarrow _1H^2 + _1e^0$	10^{11} yr
(14)	$_1H^2 + _1H^1 \rightarrow _2He^3$	2 sec
(15)	$_2He^3 + _2He^4 \rightarrow _4Be^7$	30 million yr
(16)	$_4Be^7 + _{-1}e^0 \rightarrow _3Li^7$	1 yr
(17)	$_3Li^7 + _1H^1 \rightarrow 2\,_2He^4$	1 min
(18) net result	$4\,_1H^1 + _{-1}e^0 \rightarrow _2He^4 + _1e^0$	

* See note on Table I.

The bottleneck in this noncatalyzed hydrogen fusion reaction obviously is its first step—reaction (13), which, given equal conditions, would be very much slower than the slowest step in the Bethe cycle; it can compete with the latter because hydrogen is much more abundant than carbon in the sun.

Both mechanisms of hydrogen fusion are extremely slow by our standards, and it does not seem feasible at present to create on earth conditions so much more favorable than those prevailing in the sun (that is, so much higher temperature and greater density), as to make them proceed with a speed useful for practical application.

There *are*, however, fusion reactions with lower activation energies. Some of them involve nuclei that exist on earth; others, nuclei that can be made artificially. As a first example, we can consider reaction step (17) in the second solar cycle, in which the nuclei $_3Li^7$ and $_1H^1$, both of which occur in nature, combine to form two helium nuclei, $_2He^4$. At the temperature of the sun this reaction requires only 1 minute at unit concentrations of the two reactants; and it could be accelerated by compressing the latter. Other examples of relatively easily accessible fusion reactions are those involving the heavy isotopes of hydrogen: deuterium, $_1D^2$, which is contained in all hydrogen from natural sources (see page 88), and tritium, $_1H^3$, which undergoes relatively rapid radioactive decay, and therefore must be prepared artificially —for example, by exposing the rare lithium isotope, $_3Li^6$, to neutron bombardment in an atomic reactor:

$$(19) \qquad _3Li^6 + _0n^1 \rightarrow _1H^3 + _2He^4$$

Fusion reactions analogous to reaction (13) are possible with all combinations of hydrogen isotopes. If we designate the nucleus $_1H^2$ as D (deuteron), and that of $_1H^3$ as T (triton), the possible combinations are D + H, T + H, D + D, D + T, and T + T. From the known masses of the three hydrogen isotopes, one can calculate, using Einstein's relation $E = mc^2$, the amount of energy which would be released in any one of these reactions (assuming the products to be helium nuclei and neutrons). These amounts are of the same order of magnitude as was calculated for the fusion of four ordinary H-atoms—up to 20 million electron-volts (Table III).

The activation energies required to bring about these different fusion reactions are, however, far from identical—they are lower for deuterons than for protons, and lower for tritons than for deuterons. Consequently, the temperatures needed to initiate an explosive fusion decrease as we proceed from ordinary hydrogen to deuterium and tritium. This relation is shown in Table III, the last column of which gives the velocity with which these reactions would proceed at the temperature of the sun (and unit concentration of the components).

TABLE III

		E MEV*	TIME CONSTANT†
(20)	$H + H \rightarrow D + {}_1e^0$	1.4	10^{11} yr
(21)	$D + H \rightarrow He^3$	5	0.5 sec
(22)	$T + H \rightarrow He^4$	20	0.05 sec
(23)	$D + D \rightarrow He^3 + n$	3.2	0.00003 sec
(24)	$D + D \rightarrow T + H$	4	0.00003 sec
(25)	$T + D \rightarrow He^4 + n$	17	0.0000012 sec
(26)	$T + T \rightarrow He^4 + 2 n$	11	about 0.000001 sec

* Mev stands for millions of electron-volts.
† See note on Table I.

The figures in the last column show that reactions involving only heavy hydrogen isotopes can be expected to proceed explosively—that is, within a millisecond or even a microsecond—if these hydrogen isotopes could be suddenly brought to a temperature of the order of 10 million degrees centigrade, in a highly compressed (for example, liquefied) state.

Before the advent of the atomic bomb, the production of

such temperatures under terrestrial conditions seemed out of the question. The development of the atomic bomb has changed the situation radically. The explosion of a Nagasaki-type bomb produced a fireball with a central temperature of perhaps 50 million degrees; and more powerful atomic bombs have been made since, creating larger and hotter fireballs.

Although reactions (25) and (26) are the easiest ones to initiate, and as such seem to be most suitable for the production of a thermonuclear explosion, they were unlikely to be the *main* energy-releasing reactions in early thermonuclear bombs. The reason is the previously mentioned competition between the production of tritium and plutonium. One atom of plutonium, obtained by absorbing one neutron in U-238, represents an explosive energy of 220 mev; one atom of tritium, also requiring one neutron for its formation, a power of less than 20 mev. It would therefore be wasteful to make thermonuclear bombs if for the same investment of neutrons one could get ten times more explosive power in the form of plutonium! However, it appears plausible that thermonuclear reactions not involving tritium—such as reaction (23)—could be set off by using tritium as an "intermediate detonator," in turn set off by a fission bomb. In contrast to tritium, deuterium is a stable isotope of hydrogen that can be obtained in large quantities by fractionation from natural hydrogen, at a comparatively low cost. We can therefore imagine the thermonuclear device, such as the first one exploded at Eniwetok in 1953, as containing an initial fission detonator, such as plutonium (or U-235), a "booster" detonator containing tritium, and a main charge of deuterium, or of another relatively stable thermonuclear explosive, such as lithium, perhaps combined with hydrogen in the solid compound lithium hydride.

A tempting possibility of using reaction (25) is offered by lithium deuteride. The nuclei of one lithium isotope react with those of deuterium, at the temperatures created by the fission detonator, giving tritium as a product, which reacts immediately with deuterium according to reaction (25). The high reactivity of tritium is thus made use of without the need to fabricate the latter separately, wasting pile neutrons to do so (as explained above). This process may be widely used in both American and Soviet thermonuclear bombs.

The amount of energy released by the fusion of, say, one D and one T nucleus is only about 7 per cent of that liberated by the fission of one uranium nucleus; but since the latter is fifty times heavier, the power of a "D + T explosive" would be, pound by pound, three times that of plutonium or U-235. What is more important, the amount of "fissionable" material that could be put into a single bomb is not restricted by any critical size considerations; therefore, an H-bomb can be made to any desired power specifications above those of the triggering A-bomb. "One thousand times the power of an atomic bomb" was an often-quoted figure during the years 1945-52; the first American full-scale thermonuclear test explosion at Eniwetok in 1952 was reported unofficially to have about two hundred times the force of the Hiroshima bomb; but no physical principle makes it impossible to fabricate H-bombs ten times weaker or ten or a hundred times more powerful than the "thermonuclear device" tested at Eniwetok in 1952.

Except for considerations of size (it may be impossible to assemble and transport bombs containing tens of tons of hydrogen) the thermonuclear bomb is truly "destruction unlimited." Immediately after the war there was considerable reluctance in the American atomic-energy project to pursue the development of such a weapon by an all-out crash program, likely to initiate an international race in thermonuclear arms. As a consequence, a conspiracy of silence had surrounded the superbomb between 1945 and 1950—although the scientific background of thermonuclear bombs had already been openly discussed in 1946, in a book by the Viennese theoretical physicist Hans Thirring. The question first became a matter of public concern in America in 1950, when Senator Edwin Johnson of Colorado "spilled" the hydrogen bomb story on a television show. A smoldering, behind-the-scenes controversy between the proponents of an all-out effort to develop the superbomb, represented most actively by the physicist Edward Teller, and scientists who had doubts about the advisability of this development, was thus brought into the open. Opponents argued that the development of a hydrogen bomb would increase the terror of atomic war without adding usefully to the already excessive destructive power of fission bombs—excessive in the sense that most military targets are "too small" for these bombs, so that much of their destructive power would have to be dissipated over terrain containing no objectives, or, at best, would contribute only to wholesale destruction of civilian life and property.

When, however, the Soviet Union produced its first atomic explosion, the argument that America must keep ahead of the USSR in the development of new atomic weapons, however terrible they might be, carried the day. President Truman and his military-political advisers gave the proponents of the H-bomb project the green light, and on November 1, 1952, a thermonuclear device was exploded in the Eniwetok area. This heavy, earthbound device was within a year succeeded by a bomb which could be carried by a plane, after the USSR had exploded their first such bomb in August 1953. Since then, the arms race between the United States and the USSR has concentrated on thermonuclear weapons. The Soviet Union has won it in one respect—by exploding, in 1961, a 60-megaton weapon, about three times more powerful than the biggest American tested bomb. American scientists say they, too, could have built 60-megaton bombs, but that such weapons are of no value in any "rational" military planning.

One important aspect of the Russian super-superbomb, which had over six thousand times the destructive power of the Hiroshima bomb, was that it produced relatively little radioactive "fallout." This effect of nuclear explosions had received much public attention even before the Hiroshima explosion, but came to the fore only after the development of themonuclear weapons. Fallout consists of radioactive fission products and of dust and spray raised by the explosion and made radioactive by neutrons from the bomb. The Hiroshima bomb had produced such debris, but, since the fireball did not touch the ground, the fission products were largely carried into the higher atmosphere and dissipated there by the winds. In a later underwater test in the Bikini lagoon, water containing radioactive fission products was sprayed over the target ships and made them uninhabitable for months or years.

A thermonuclear explosion, however, produces no radioactive fission products, except for those caused by the fission detonator. It was therefore expected that thermonuclear weapons would be relatively "clean"; but an H-bomb test in 1954 at Eniwetok created an extremely heavy fallout, revealed to the world by the plight of the Japanese crew of the fishing boat *Lucky Dragon,* miles away from the explosion site. Subsequently it was revealed that the tested weapon had been a fission-fusion-fission bomb, in which a fission detonator and a fusion charge were supplemented by a fission jacket, containing uranium-238. This was a truly devilish invention: the neutrons produced by fusion—see reactions (23) and (25) on page 192—are fast enough to fission the so-called "unfissionable" uranium-238. The larger part of the explosive power of such bombs originated from the third stage, composed of readily available ordinary uranium, which made this type of H-bomb unexpectedly cheap—but extremely "dirty." The amount of fission products it spewed out corresponded to its total fission yield—that is, to megatons, rather than to kilotons, of explosive power.

Radiation poisoning thus became a lethal factor of great significance in nuclear-war planning. The most horrendous pictures of an all-destroying nuclear war are based on the possibility of spreading radioactive fallout over whole continents. Ever since, there have been hints of the development of "cleaner" thermonuclear bombs as powerful as the 1954 fission-fusion-fission bomb, but with a lesser fission component. The Russian 60-megaton bomb demonstrated that the Soviet Union has developed such weapons.

If thermonuclear bombs should be exploded in a full-scale war of the future, the cities of the belligerent nations may well be wiped out completely, and the radioactive products of the explosions, settling on the ground, may produce both extensive immediate damage and deep effects on the hereditary properties of all plant and animal life exposed to their radiations.

XI

ATTEMPTS TO OUTLAW ATOMIC BOMBS FAIL

For most people the mysteries of chemistry, biology, or electronics are not less bewildering than those of atomic fission or fusion, but for scientists the difference between events in which only whole atoms, molecules, or free electrons are involved, and those in which the nuclei of the atoms are split, disintegrated, or combined, is overwhelming. For them there never was a question that with the first atomic oven fired at Chicago on December 2, 1942, a new era in history had begun.

Like our own bodies, the world around us is, in the main, a world of chemistry. When man first lighted a fire, he was making use of a chemical force which was to endanger him occasionally but which in the long run he could control. The nuclear fire, let loose, may one day wipe life off the face of the earth. Since attempts to keep it a monopoly of a single nation were doomed to rapid failure because of the universality of scientific progress, which does not stop at national boundaries, mankind can be made safe from atomic fire hazard only by putting atomic energy under world-wide control, which would make its use for destructive purposes impossible.

This conclusion was reached in the earliest discussions of the political and military implications of atomic energy behind the walls of the Manhattan Project laboratories. In March 1945 Leo Szilard sent a memorandum to President Roosevelt, in which he said of the first A-bombs to be perfected:

These bombs will be much less powerful than the ones we now know can be made, and in all likelihood will be made later; yet the first bomb that is detonated over Japan will be spectacular enough to start a race in atomic armaments between us and other nations.

For a few years after that, we shall almost certainly be ahead of Russia. But even if we assume that we could keep ahead of her in this development all the time, this may neither offer us protection from attack nor give us substantial advantage in case of war.

The weakness in the position of the United States is in the very high concentration of its manufacturing capacity and population in cities. The destruction of the cities may easily mean the end of our ability to resist.

One of the questions that has to be considered is whether it might be possible to set up some system of controls of the production of these [fissionable] materials. Whether it is politically and technically feasible to set up effective controls, and what we could do to improve our chances in this respect, are questions that urgently require study and decisions.

As to our chances of persuading the Russians to accept mutual control, much may depend on the proper timing of our approach to Russia; it would appear that such an approach would have to be made *immediately after we demonstrated the potency of atomic bombs.*

Similar ideas were presented in a report submitted in June 1945 to the Secretary of War by a "Committee on Social and Political Implications" set up at the Chicago laboratories of the Atomic Energy Project. This Franck report—so called after the chairman of the committe, the Nobel Prize-winning physicist James Franck—said:

Among all the arguments calling for an efficient international organization for peace, the existence of nuclear weapons is the most compelling one. In the absence of an international authority which would make all resort to force in international conflicts impossible, nations could still be diverted from a path which must lead to total mutual destruction, by a specific international agreement barring a nuclear armaments race.

If no efficient international agreement is achieved, the race for nuclear armaments will be on . . . after our first demonstration of the existence of nuclear weapons. After this, it might take other nations three or four years to overcome our present head-start, and eight or ten years to draw even with us, even if we should continue to do intensive work in this field. This might be all the time we will have to bring about the relocation of our population and industry.

The report then considered two different possibilities of international control:

Given mutual trust and willingness on all sides to give up a certain part of their sovereign rights, by admitting international control of certain phases of national economy, the control could be exercised (alternatively or simultaneously) on two different levels.

The first and perhaps simplest way is to ration the raw materials—primarily, the uranium ores. The amounts of ore taken out of the ground at different locations could be controlled, and each nation could be allotted only an amount which would make large-scale separation of fissionable isotopes impossible.

Such a limitation would have the drawback of making impossible also the development of nuclear power for peacetime purposes.

An agreement on a higher level, involving more mutual trust

and understanding, would be to allow unlimited production, but keep exact bookkeeping on the fate of each pound of uranium ores.

The report continued:

We believe that these considerations make the use of nuclear bombs for an early unannounced attack against Japan inadvisable. If the United States were to be first to release this new means of indiscriminate destruction on mankind, she would sacrifice public support throughout the world, precipitate the race for armaments, and prejudice the possibility of reaching an international agreement on the future control of such weapons.

Much more favorable conditions for the eventual achievement of such an agreement could be created if nuclear bombs were first revealed to the world by a demonstration in an appropriately selected uninhabited area.

The views of American statesmen, preoccupied with the immediate problem of winning the war, evolved more slowly and hesitatingly. Secretary of War Stimson mentions in his memoirs[1] that on March 15, 1945, he had a conversation with President Roosevelt about the "two schools of thought that exist in respect to the future control after the war of this project, in case it is successful, one of them being the secret close-in attempted control of the project by those who control it now, and the other being international control based upon freedom of science." This formulation foreshadowed the wrong light in which many political leaders were inclined to see the atomic-energy dilemma: as if America had the choice of keeping or not keeping the atomic bomb for herself and the main reason for "sharing" it with other nations was the idea of freedom of science!

[1] *On Active Service in War and Peace,* by Henry L. Stimson and McGeorge Bundy (New York: Harper & Bros., 1948).

After Truman succeeded Roosevelt, the question was turned over to a committee with Secretary of War Stimson as chairman and James F. Byrnes, Ralph A. Bard, William L. Clayton, Vannevar Bush, and James B. Conant as members.

Having consulted with its scientific advisers—including A. H. Compton, E. Fermi, E. O. Lawrence, and J. R. Oppenheimer—the committee recommended on June 1, 1945, "that the first bombs should be used against Japan as soon as available; that they should be used on military installations, or war plants surrounded by or adjacent to, other buildings susceptible to damage, and that they should be used without prior warning of the nature of the weapon." (Later Mr. Bard dissented on the last point.) What followed at Hiroshima and Nagasaki in August 1945 is history.

On September 11, 1945, a month after the two bombs were dropped on Japan, Mr. Stimson recommended to the President that direct negotiations be undertaken with the Soviet Union about the future of atomic energy. He said that unless the Soviet Union is "voluntarily invited into partnership upon a basis of cooperation and trust," feverish activity will be stimulated in Russia toward the development of this bomb, "leading to a secret armament race of rather a desperate character." He continued:

Whether Russia gets control of the necessary secrets of production in a minimum of, say, four years or a maximum of twenty years is not nearly as important to the world and civilization as to make sure that when they do get it they are willing and cooperative partners among the peace-loving nations of the world. It is true, if we approach them now, as I would propose, we may be gambling on their good faith and risk their getting into production of bombs a little sooner than they would otherwise.

To put the matter concisely, I consider the problem of our satisfactory relations with Russia as not merely connected with but as virtually dominated by the problem of the atomic bomb.

I think the bomb . . . constitutes merely a first step in a new control by man over the forces of nature too revolutionary and dangerous to fit into the old concepts. I think it really caps the climax of the race between man's growing technical power for destructiveness and his psychological power of self-control and group control—his moral power. If so, our method of approach to the Russians is a question of the most vital importance in the evolution of human progress.[2]

Other leaders of American policy in 1945 did not have the same sense of urgency. For a while the Administration gave little evidence of what it intended to do. On October 3, President Truman proposed to initiate discussions, first with Great Britain and Canada, and then with other nations, saying that "the hope of civilization lies in international arrangements looking, if possible, to the renunciation of the use and development of the atomic bomb, and directing and encouraging the use of atomic energy and all future scientific information toward peaceful and humanitarian ends." On October 27, however, he said that the United States intends to "keep the atomic bomb in sacred trust on behalf of all mankind."

Only on November 15, 1945, did the heads of the governments of the United States, Great Britain, and Canada— President Truman, and Prime Ministers Attlee and King— announce that the establishment of international control of atomic energy was the official aim of their policy. Instead of negotiating with the Soviet Union on this subject, as proposed by Secretary Stimson, they threw the problem into the lap of the newly formed United Nations. On December 16,

[2] *Op. cit.*

the foreign ministers of America and Great Britain, Byrnes and Bevin, met Soviet foreign minister Molotov in Moscow, and obtained, without difficulty, the adherence of the Soviet Union to the plan of establishing a United Nations committee to consider international control of atomic energy "to the extent necessary to insure its use only for peaceful purposes."

On January 3, 1946, this proposal was adopted unanimously by the United Nations General Assembly. However, it took the nations elected to this committee—which included among its twelve members the so-called Big Five and Canada—several months to choose their representatives, and when they were appointed, it became clear that with the exception of the American representative, Bernard Baruch, the committee was simply the Security Council of the United Nations, sitting around a different table.

Looking back, one can perhaps trace the deadlock of the control negotiations to these early days when national governments (and the Soviet government above all), instead of entrusting the formulation of the control agreement to politically unencumbered experts, resolved to keep it in the hands of their political emissaries.

The UN Atomic Energy Committee first convened on June 14, 1946. In the meantime, the State Department had appointed a committee (Dean Acheson, Vannevar Bush, James B. Conant, General Leslie R. Groves, and J. J. McCloy) to consider the proposals which America might submit to the UN commission, and they in turn appointed a panel of consultants, with David E. Lilienthal as chairman, and two scientists (J. R. Oppenheimer and Charles R. Thomas), and two industrialists (Chester I. Barnard and Harry A. Winne) as members. This panel evolved a document which became known as the "Acheson-Lilienthal report." Its revolutionary idea was that international control can only be made a success if it is based not on police-type supervision, but on a common effort to develop atomic energy for peaceful purposes. Instead of UN inspectors investigating whether or not national or private atomic-energy establishments divert fissionable materials to the fabrication of weapons, the report proposed that a UN-sponsored, internationally staffed agency should assume a world-wide monopoly of the production of fissionable materials, and that all private or national atomic activities be prohibted except on a non-dangerous, small scale. The UN atomic agency was to strive for rapid development of atomic power everywhere, with particular consideration of the economic requirements of the individual nations.

The American delegation to the UN Atomic Energy Commission (UNAEC), headed by Mr. Baruch, adopted the Acheson-Lilienthal plan in all essential features, adding only one new provision—that violations of the control agreement should be dealt with by the UN without the application of the "big power" veto.

In this form, the proposal was introduced by Mr. Baruch in the opening session of UNAEC on June 14, 1946. In a memorable speech, Mr. Baruch admonished the committee that "we are here to make a choice between the quick and the dead."

In its first answer to the American proposal, the Soviet delegation called it unacceptable "in whole or in part," and proposed instead a pact outlawing the production and use of atomic bombs and ordering the destruction of existing bombs within 90 days. Violation of the pact was to be considered an "international crime." The methods of implementation of the pact were left to "future negotiations"; the punishment of violators was to be reserved to the Security Council, and subject to the usual veto by the big nations.

While this beginning looked unpromising, some hopeful developments followed when the UN committee passed the ball to a group of technical experts, including two Russian physicists. On September 27, 1946, this group produced a unanimous report setting forth the technical requirements of an effective control system—the last unanimously agreed document in this area. On December 31, 1946, Mr. Baruch submitted the draft of a first report of the UNAEC to the General Assembly, which combined this "feasibility memorandum" of the technical experts, with the main features of the "American plan." It was adopted by a vote of 10 to 0 in the committee, with the Soviet Union and Poland abstaining.

A hopeful moment came when, on February 18, 1947, the Soviet delegate submitted a set of amendments to this report. By this move, the Soviet Union seemed to have abandoned its position that the American plan was unacceptable "in whole or in part," and agreed to consider it an appropriate basis for negotiations.

However, the hope was dashed a few weeks later, when, on March 5, 1946, the Soviet delegate denounced the principle of managerial control, which the experts agreed was essential for effectiveness of the control function. He called it a conspiracy of American monopolies to prevent the industrial development of atomic energy everywhere, and in the Soviet Union in particular.

This practically ended all round-table discussion of the control plan in the United Nations. Instead, the majority proceeded to evolve on its own a more detailed blueprint along the lines of the American plan, in the hope that such an elaboration, with safeguards protecting the interests of individual nations, might sooner or later prove acceptable to the Soviet Union. This work was terminated, and a second report adopted by the committee, on September 11, 1947, by a vote of 10 to 1 (Soviet Union), with Poland abstaining.

This second report of the UNAEC constitutes the most detailed and realistic document on the subject of international control produced by the committee. It differs from the Acheson-Lilienthal draft by much stronger awareness of the danger of accumulation of large stocks of fissionable materials in places where they can be seized by national governments. It provides that "dangerous facilities" (that is, factories and plants which contain or can produce large amounts of nuclear explosives) should be permitted only as world conditions warrant, and where economic justification exists. Supplies of nuclear fuels shall be provided only for power plants whose location, design, and financing have been definitely settled, and approved by the UN authority. The distribution of stocks and facilities among nations should be in accordance with quotas to be agreed upon simultaneously with the conclusion of the control convention. Elaborate safeguards were introduced into the mechanisms for the inspection of existing atomic plants and for the detection of clandestine activities, to avoid their use for economic espionage. To prevent such investigations from causing international tensions, it was suggested that a certain fraction of the territory of each nation should be surveyed routinely each year, so that a survey does not imply suspicion.

In parallel with the elaboration of this "UN majority control plan," the committee continued for some time a desultory discussion of the amendments suggested by the Soviet delegation to the first report. A more important parallel development began on June 11, 1947, when the Soviet Union submitted its own proposal for control, spelling out, for the first time, the ideas vaguely anticipated a year earlier in their statement before the opening meeting of the committee.

The essence of the Soviet plan was the establishment of a UN control commission with the right to inspect atomic-energy activities in various countries and to make sure that these were not directed toward the production of atomic weapons. The volume of national activities, and the stocks of fissionable material which individual nations could accumulate, was to remain unrestricted. (On several occasions, the Soviet representatives had agreed to the principle of quotas; later, however, Vishinsky rejected this principle as interfering with the economic sovereignty of nations.) Two types of inspection were specified in the Soviet proposal—"periodical" routine inspection and "special investigation"— the latter to be undertaken only when legitimate suspicion of violation exists. In a final concession, made considerably later, the Soviet Union conceded that routine inspection could be "continuous," rather than "periodical."

The Soviet proposals stated that international inspecting teams should have the right of free entry into and egress from all countries, and access to all officially acknowledged atomic-energy establishments within them. The day-by-day decisions of the UN control commission—including the ordering of special investigations—were to be made by simple majority; but the Soviet Union insisted that sanctions against violators of the control agreement should be reserved to the Security Council, where the veto right prevails.

No further progress toward international control has been made since the elaboration of the UN majority "management plan" in 1946-47, and the outlining of the Soviet "inspection plan" in 1947-48. In the Third Report of the Security Council (on May 17, 1948), the UN Atomic Energy Commission recommended the suspension of its activity. The Commission was asked to resume it by a UN Assembly resolution on November 4, 1948, but again acknowledged deadlock on July 25, 1949, about the time that the first atomic bomb test took place in the Soviet Union.

For a considerable length of time, the United States had insisted on dealing with the atomic weapons independently from other, so-called "conventional" weapons. It was hoped that the novelty of the problem would permit a fresh approach, such as the international development effort proposed in the Acheson-Lilienthal blueprint, and that the success of this approach could provide an opening wedge for future agreements in other fields. The Soviet Union, on the other hand, insisted from the beginning on including atomic weapons in the general discussion of disarmament. When, however, the United States (and other Western nations) finally decided that the attempt to solve the problem of atomic weapons separately had failed and proposed the merger of the UN Atomic Energy Committee with the UN Committee on Conventional Armaments, the Soviet Union, in reversal of its previous stand, insisted—unsuccessfully— that the UNAEC should be kept alive as a separate unit. That the combined UN Committee on Disarmament has made no more progress after the merger than the two separate committees had achieved separately before was hardly unexpected.

On December 8, 1953, spurred by the successful development of the thermonuclear weapon by both the United States and the USSR, President Eisenhower, in a speech to the General Assembly of the UN, made a move to break the deadlock in atomic negotiations. He suggested forgetting for the time being the ambitious attempt effectively to abolish atomic weapons (through international management or international inspection) and to take instead a step toward the relaxation of the atomic arms race by creating a small pool of fissionable materials, to which all nations contribute, and a UN agency to administer this pool in the interest of nations particularly anxious to develop atomic power.

Thus, the International Atomic Energy Agency (IAEA) was established, with a seat in Vienna, Austria, but the first decade of its existence was disappointing. Not only did it exert no influence on the nuclear-arms race, but even the development of nuclear reactors for peaceful purposes largely bypassed it, as the major nuclear powers dealt directly, by bilateral agreements, with smaller nations anxious for assistance in the development of nuclear energy. Subsequently, however, the big nuclear powers showed willingness to give the IAEA the responsibility for supervising peaceful nuclear reactors, in order to make sure that they are not diverted to the production of weapon-grade materials. The United States showed the way by voluntarily placing under IAEA supervision its power reactor at Rowe, Massachusetts.

While atomic disarmament still remained the official aim of both United States and Soviet foreign policy, after a decade of disarmament negotiations, the only practical achievement was the limited test ban, extended to all but underground tests. This at least prevented any further environmental contamination by long-lived radioactive isotopes of cesium, strontium, and other elements with a tendency to accumulate in living organisms (radiostrontium mixing with its homologue, calcium, in cells and tissue fluids). It also may have slowed down somewhat the development of anti-missile missiles and of other new large-yield nuclear weapons, since only relatively small-scale explosions can be conveniently tested in underground chambers.

Realizing the difficulty of reliable identification and dismantling of all nuclear weapons in case of an agreement on nuclear disarmament, first the American experts, and more recently also the Soviet negotiators, have proposed schemes referred to in the United States as "arms control" and in the Soviet Union as "nuclear umbrella." These schemes envisage leaving to each major nuclear nation a relatively small number of "legitimate" nuclear weapons, with the means for their safe delivery, such as underground or submarine missile launchers. This arrangement would guarantee that the nations carrying out the agreed destruction of their weapons would not find themselves suddenly confronted at any stage of disarmament with the possible threat of preserved nuclear weapons on the other side, and with no capacity for a counter-threat of nuclear retaliation. The destruction of these legitimate weapons would then be left to the last stage of disarmament, in which unlimited freedom of inspection would be granted by both sides. Soviet-American agreement on this principle is one of the few faintly promising developments in the exasperating disarmament negotiations going on and on at Geneva.

XII

ATOMIC POWER EMERGES

What sets fissionable materials apart from the conventional chemical explosives and fuels is the enormously greater *concentration* of their energy: concentration in space, if one thinks of using them as fuels, and in both space and time, if they are to be used as explosives.

It may be that in the future man will discover applications of fissionable materials—in addition to destruction of life and property in war—for which this unique concentration will be decisive. Some thoughtful physicists—the Austrian, Hans Thirring, among them—have argued that as long as no such applications are known, our duty is to conserve fissionable materials and not to waste them on "trivial" tasks which can be performed equally well by chemical fuels, falling water, or sunlight. To use atomic power to turn the wheels of industry, or atomic heat to smelt ores, would be, in this opinion, a dissipation of irreplaceable assets. If all economically available uranium were to be spent for such purposes by generations which know of no better use for it, our descendants might find the planet bare of a material whose unique possibilities had never been fully realized.

Among the applications of atomic fuel that does some justice to the compactness of this power source is the nuclear propulsion of submarines. (This, incidentally, was the first application of nuclear power suggested by scientists on the Manhattan Project immediately after the invention of the nuclear reactor in 1943.) This idea was picked up and pressed to a successful conclusion by Admiral Hyman Rickover.

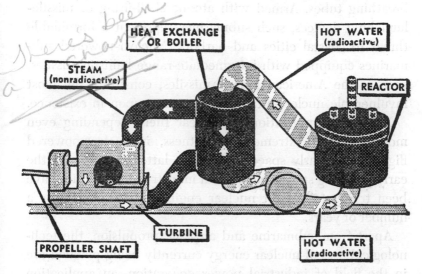

FIGURE 22. PLAN OF AN ATOMIC POWER PLANT

The three main parts: reactor, heat-exchanger, and turbine, are shown. Recent plans suggest the possibility of eliminating the intermediate heat-exchanger. (Courtesy of the New York Times.)

The world's first nuclear-powered submarine, the U.S.N.S. *Nautilus,* was launched in 1954. Since then, the fleet of American nuclear submarines has grown to a dozen or more, and their amazing capacities were demonstrated by such feats as underwater cruises to the North Pole. The Soviet Union also has a fleet of such vessels, and England and France are in the process of acquiring prototypes of nuclear submarines. Since the nuclear fuel lasts practically indefinitely and requires no oxygen, nuclear submarines are able to cruise around the world without refueling, or even surfacing, except to relieve the strain of underwater life on the crew. The threat of such submarines to surface navigation will be much more difficult to combat than that of the U-boats in World War II, even those equipped with "snorkel" breathing tubes. Armed with atomic shell-firing or missile-launching devices, such submarines represent a formidable threat to coastal cities and harbors. Nuclear-powered submarines equipped with intermediate-range ballistic missiles, such as the American Polaris missiles, constitute the most invulnerable nuclear-attack retaliation weapon in existence.

A possible application of nuclear fuels, depending even more on their extreme compactness, is nuclear-powered flight, particularly space flight. The latter is as yet in the early-planning stages, but several industrial laboratories have been trying to perfect nuclear engines for airplanes for a number of years.

Apart from submarine and airplane propulsion, the technological uses of nuclear energy currently being pursued are in the field of industrial power generation—an application in which the unique concentration of this energy usually is immaterial, and sometimes even a hindrance, because of the high requirements it makes on the heat-dissipation devices. Exceptions are locations which are too remote or too inaccessible to justify transportation of coal or oil, or transmission of electrical energy, and where only the practically weightless atomic fuels may make industrial development possible.

In America, where the supply of chemical fuels is for the time being adequate and atomic power has therefore little if any immediate economic justification, the development of industrial atomic power is spurred mainly by the desire to stay in the van of progress. It is often argued that the United States cannot concede to another nation—particularly the Soviet Union—leadership in the development of an art which power-deficient nations of Asia or South America may be eager to utilize for their industrialization.

The drive to develop power plants received further impetus from a continuing upward revision of earlier estimates of the available uranium resources. When the possible role of atomic energy in industry was first discussed in 1945, it was estimated, on the basis of the high-grade deposits of uranium ore then known (in the Belgian Congo and in Northern Canada), as being very limited. More recently, however, the attitude of those in touch with uranium procurement has become progressively more sanguine. The figures on which this optimism is based remain secret, but three general reasons for it are apparent. One is the discovery of new, apparently major high-grade uranium deposits—for example, in Saskatchewan in Canada (near Lake Athabaska, a few hundred miles southwest of the famous Eldorado mines on Great Bear Lake), and in Australia (Radium Hill, Rum Jungle). The second reason is the successful exploitation of "medium-grade" raw materials, such as the carnotites of the Colorado plateau, and of low-grade sources, such as the South African gold ores (especially the "tailings" accumulated from the extraction of gold in the past). The Union of South Africa, in particular, is at present one of the major suppliers. Raw materials of even lower uranium content, such as certain phosphate rocks, have been investigated as potential sources of uranium, with some promise of success. Palmer Putnam, who made on behalf of the Atomic Energy Commission an extensive study of the world reserves of energy, came up in

1953 with the amazing estimate that the world resources of commercially utilizable fissionable materals are fifty times greater than the world resources of commercially utilizable fossil fuels!

Putnam's estimate included *all* uranium—uranium-238 as well as uranium-235—and thorium. The justification for their inclusion lies in the possibility of "breeding" fissionable isotopes, plutonium-239 and uranium-233, from the main isotopes of the two elements, uranium-238 and thorium-232. The success of the breeding idea was an important source of optimism for the atomic power program. By 1964 plans were under way for a joint European-American experimental breeding reactor to be installed in the United States.

Breeding, by analogy with the significance of the word in husbandry, means producing new fissionable material (plutonium-239 from uranium-238, or uranium-233 from thorium-232) in a quanity *larger* than that of the U-235 consumed in the maintenance of the chain reaction. Fission of one U-235 nucleus produces, on the average, approximately 2.5 neutrons; of one Pu-239 nucleus, about 3 neutrons. In a reactor, one of these neutrons is needed to keep the reaction chain going; while the remaining 1.5 to 2 neutrons are available for the conversion of U-238 into Pu-239 (or of Th-232 into U-233). Since this number is greater than one, it is in principle possible to produce more than one new fissionable nucleus for each nucleus consumed. The practical feasibility of breeding depends on whether the losses of neutrons (by escape from the reactor, or by absorption in the various pile constituents, such as its structural elements and the progressively accumulating fission products), can be kept sufficiently low, and the yield of chemical extraction of the newly formed fissionable products—plutonium-239 or uranium-233—can be made sufficiently high, for the margin of 0.5 to 1 neutron per fission not to be lost in the cycle. Only if this high-efficiency operation proves possible, will the actual amount of new fissionable material derived from the cycle become greater than the amount invested in it. The chemical part of the cycle, in particular, is of decisive importance—probably never in the history of chemical industry has there been such a premium on having the recovery yield of a product close to 100 per cent. A loss of a few per cent in the complicated purification process could make, in this case, all the difference between success and failure.

The Atomic Energy Commission has announced that the technical feasibility of making the capital of fissionable material invested in a pile actually grow, has been proved. We don't know yet whether the costs of a breeding cycle—putting the material into a reactor, running the latter until sufficient new fissionable material has been "bred," extracting the latter, and re-inserting it into the same or another reactor —will be economically attractive in the near future. In principle, however, the success of the breeding process has made *all* uranium and thorium potential nuclear fuels.

On several occasions in the past few years the U. S. Atomic Energy Commission has asked industrial leaders to consider the possibility of private industry's becoming actively interested in the production of atomic power. The reaction was cautious; industry felt that it lacks sufficient information to judge the possibilities, that the capital needed for the development might be too large for a private concern, and the risk of failure too great. In 1952 and 1953, a more active interest began to be apparent, and several groups of industrial firms proposed more or less specific plans for the development of private industrial atomic power. These plans can be divided into two groups. One aims at the construction of "single-purpose" atomic power stations—that is, plants in which natural uranium, or uranium enriched in fissionable components (at first loaned or sold by the U. S. government), would be "loaned" for the production of electrical energy for commercial purposes, without attempting also to use the same reactors for the fabrication of new fissionable material. Two kinds of such single-purpose power plants have been envisaged: small—perhaps even mobile—installations, which could be useful in areas remote from conventional sources of power; and large stationary central electrical power stations.

Contrasted to these pure atomic power plants are "double-purpose" plants for simultaneous production of atomic power and new fissionable materials. The idea is to make the otherwise excessively expensive electrical power production from nuclear fuels more economical by selling the by-product fissionable material back to the Atomic Energy Commission, presumably for use in the weapons program.

While there can be little objection—except along the lines of a cautious conservation argument—to the private construction of single-purpose atomic power plants, the combination of private generation of atomic power with the fabrication of atomic explosives raises certain questions. Even apart from the security problems involved, the advisability of creating a private atomic power industry with a vested interest in continued production of atomic explosives calls for scrutiny. It has been suggested, by Gordon Dean, then chairman of the Atomic Energy Commission, among others (but contradicted by other, equally qualified experts), that the American stock of nuclear explosives may soon reach a level sufficient for all conceivable military requirements, or that the rate of production of these explosives in government plants in existence or under construction will soon be sufficient to assure all the needed addition to the stockpile. If this is the case, then the U. S. government is not in a position to make long-range commitments to private firms for the purchase of plutonium (or uranium-233) for military needs. Of course, these products, if not needed for military purposes, could be made available for enrichment of natural uranium, or for direct use of fuel, in industrial atomic furnaces; but this use may not justify the high prices acceptable for military procurement. Considerations of this kind have caused the AEC to reject private industrial plans for dual-purpose reactors. On the other hand, no private group has as yet declared itself ready to commit enough funds for the development of a single-purpose nuclear power plant. The AEC therefore decided to undertake the next step itself, and contracted with a private firm (Westinghouse) for the construction of a single-purpose nuclear power reactor at the government's expense. However, a private firm (Duquesne Light Company) constructed the electric power plant in which the heat produced in this reactor is converted into electrical energy. This power plant, built under the direction of Admiral Rickover, is located at Shippingport, Pennsylvania. A few other industry-sponsored nuclear-power plants have been placed in operation, and others are in different stages of planning or construction.

In countries such as Great Britain, where coal is rising in price because of exhaustion of the richer and more easily accessible veins, and India, where deposits of mineral fuels appear insufficient for large-scale industrialization programs, the development of industrial atomic power is anticipated with more justifiable eagerness than in the United States.

India, which possesses large deposits of thorium-bearing monazite, seems to be prepared to invest large amounts of money in developing an atomic power industry utilizing these national resources.

In August 1956, the Soviet Union announced the operation of the world's first nuclear-power electric station, in the Kaluga province, not far from Moscow. The USSR entertained vast plans for other, much larger power stations, but economic pressures have forced a slowdown, so that in the next seven years only one large power-producing reactor, near the Urals, was reported to have begun operation.

In principle, the production of power from nuclear energy is no different from the conversion into mechanical or electrical energy of any other kind of heat. In practice, however, serious problems arise. A heat engine is the more efficient the greater the temperature difference between the boiler and the condenser. This requires high-temperature-resistant structural materials. In a nuclear engine, another requirement is added: these materials have also to have suitable nuclear properties—for example, they must not grab too eagerly the precious neutrons needed for the economy of the cycle. Entirely new metals and ceramics have had to be investigated. Zirconium has already emerged from this study as an important new structural metal.

A second problem, raised by the intense radioactivity that prevails in the reactor, is that of the resistance of structural materials to radiation. As an example of the dangers involved, we may mention the changes in shape, volume, and mechanical properties which graphite, used as moderator in the plutonium-producing piles, undergoes after prolonged irradiation. These effects have caused grave anxieties to those in charge of the Hanford plutonium works.

A third problem is the protection of people from radiation. "Shielding" the reactor as a whole—for example, by several feet of concrete—is the answer to the danger to personnel from the radiation emitted by the chain-reacting core; but if the reactor is to serve as source of power, a vapor or liquid must be conducted through it to collect the fission heat and take it outside to drive a steam engine or a turbine. This coolant becomes radioactive as it passes through the reactor. Therefore, it becomes difficult to use it directly for the operation of the power unit. A third structure is therefore inserted between the reactor and the power plant—a *heat exchanger*, in which the hot radioactive fluid that emerges from the reactor can transfer its heat to another fluid, circulating in an independent, closed cycle (see Figure 22).

A few words should be said about "taming" the H-bomb and producing useful energy by means of controlled thermonuclear reactions. If this could be accomplished, the long-range prospects of mankind would be improved. The reserves of uranium and thorium ore for fission power may be several times larger than those of the fossil fuels, coal and oil, used for conventional electric or steam power, but these ores, too, are limited. Fission power could extend the lifetime of industrial civilization on earth by only a few thousand years. Fusion power, on the other hand, could be derived from deuterium, of which there is a practically unlimited supply in the oceans. The only other unlimited energy supply on earth is sunlight, but while the use of nuclear energy presents the problem of "too much in too small a volume in too short a time," the energy of sunlight is "too little spread over too wide an area over too long a time." Thus far, the problem of highly concentrated power has been easier to deal with than that of extremely dilute power.

In the late 1950s, the possibility of controlling fusion power seemed to be near. The main question of how to bring a gas to a temperature of many millions of degrees and to keep it confined at that temperature, without melting its container, was solved simultaneously in the United States and the Soviet Union by the invention of the "magnetic bottle." In this device powerful magnetic forces keep the reacting gas away from the walls of the vessel. However, the practical problem of stabilizing such an extremely hot gas, called "plasma," in which the outer electrons are stripped from the atoms by thermal collisions, has proved very difficult, and research teams in the United States, Great Britain, and the Soviet Union are making progress by almost infinitesimally small steps forward. After this problem is solved technologically—as it will be—the next question is how to make fusion power economical—that is, how to apply the energy liberated in the "magnetic bottle" to produce electricity or industrial heat at a competitive cost.

But even with these great problems unsolved, the release of thermonuclear energy has brought enormous change in the status of mankind in the universe. We suddenly can see the future of civilization extended from a few thousand to many millions of years—if mankind will manage not to destroy itself in the conflagration of a nuclear war.

... ...

EPILOGUE TO THE REVISED EDITION

By EUGENE RABINOWITCH

Obviously, the stage in the development of atomic power at which the narrative in the preceding chapter has to stop is not one of achievement, but rather one of hopeful beginning. Many years will pass before it becomes clear to what extent atomic power will affect the economy of the different nations —from fully industrialized and coal-rich North America to industrially backward and coal-deficient South America and southwest Asia. Many exciting applications of presently known principles such as nuclear "breeding" are likely to lie ahead; and exciting new discoveries are not impossible. One has only to think of the remote but not altogether excluded possibility of controlled thermonuclear reactions.

All this adds up to a fascinating outlook for the not too distant industrial future. But as we advance along the various inviting roads into the unknown landscape of the atomic-powered world, a great and ominous shadow obscures our progress: the shadow of a war fought with atomic and thermonuclear weapons. Atomic power plants, ships, and airplanes are largely future promises; but nuclear bombs are dread realities. If freely used in a future major war, they will wipe out not only whatever atomic technology mankind may have developed by then, but the whole of our already existing industrial civilization as well. Even if we move much faster than we have done so far in dispersing our industrial plants from the big metropolitan areas, and erecting radar and guided-missile screens around our shores and cities, an atomic war will still mean a toll of life counted in tens of millions, and will produce enormous destruction in every country taking part in it—not to speak of possible long-range hereditary radiation damage to the human race, and to all life on earth. It is a solemn choice that faces the leaders of mankind—and their peoples, in the countries where people have a say about what their leaders are doing. Mankind has lived through war after war in the past, with peace merely an interval between wars; it now suddenly faces the absolute necessity of living in peace in the future, or committing something closely akin to the suicidal drive of lemmings into the sea. Such a transition to a new era in human relations would have been difficult enough in the kind of world that existed before the First World War, when the political ideals and forms of political organization of the nations were much more similar, and not as mutually exclusive as they are now. It is an appallingly difficult task at a time when powerful states are dedicated to the idea of unifying the world under an economic and political system abhorrent to most peoples. But however forbidding these difficulties, it is better to face them with a clear understanding than to attempt to ignore them, and to pretend that nations can continue living, in a world of atomic and nuclear weapons, in the same way as they did "before the bomb," resorting from time to time to wars as "continuation of policies with other means," in the famous dictum of Clausewitz.

Dr. Hecht concluded the first edition of this book in 1946 with the following sentences, which are still valid:

A wonderful tool has been made available, and vast stores of energy have been opened that can keep us going perhaps even after coal and oil reserves have been exhausted. It is significant to remember that ultimately the energy from coal, oil, and water power is atomic energy. Water power comes from the sun's heat; coal and oil are only the remains of ancient plants that grew by the light of the sun. The light and heat of the sun are ours from the atomic transformation of hydrogen into helium. Now we need no longer use green plants alone to capture the atomic energy released in the sun; we can release it ourselves by the fission of uranium.

All this, however, is idle speculation and fancy dreaming so long as the threat of war hangs over us. Man really has his fate in his hands. If he can put into the practice of world relations the same honesty, the same courage, the same intellect, and the same drive that have gone into science and the accumulation of knowledge, then the future will indeed be a happy one. If he cannot, then anyone can envision the hell that may be on earth. The menace of total destruction, the horror of partial survival, the distortion of daily life, that the new weapons envisage may easily convert an uncertain political and economic environment into what Castiglioni calls a "collective anguish" comparable to the tenth century's terror of the world's end.

Only the conviction of a just and stable peace, the removal of fear and tension, and the recognition of all men's right to survive regardless of color and creed can make a world in which atomic energy can be properly used.

Whether these desiderata can be achieved by the continued division of the world into sovereign and independent nations is dubious. We live on the continuous but finite surface of a sphere of which any part can be reached from any other part in a few hours. It is obsolete to suppose that such a surface can be artificially maintained in a fractional state of national groups, each determined to keep its peculiar economy free from influence by the others. The sooner all peoples join in some law-abiding extra-national order, the better for us who hope for civilization. If the advent of atomic energy succeeds in making us acutely aware of the need for a legal world order, it will have been good, in spite of its horrid face at Hiroshima. I hope the future will see it as good.

These words remain as valid in 1964 as they were in 1946.

INDEX